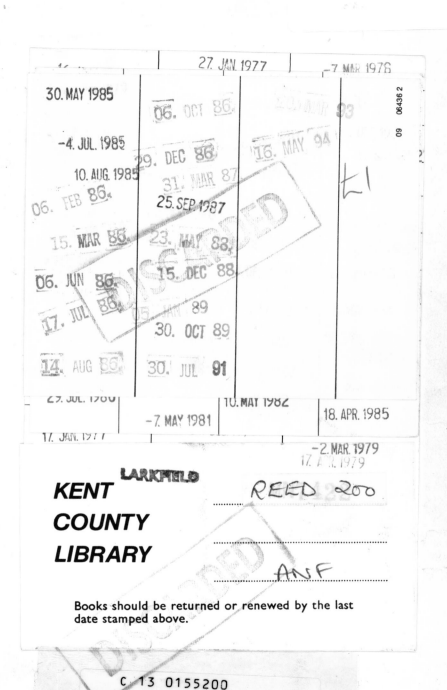

# 150 Years of British Steam Locomotives

One of the outstanding designs in 157 years of British
steam locomotive construction: C. B. Collett's Castle
class 4-6-0 on the Great Western, introduced in 1923
was built in batches until 1950. No 5043 then named
*Earl of Mount Edgcumbe* seen here at the head of a
Cheltenham – Paddington train in June 1936 was built
earlier that year. (Locomotive & General Railway
Photographs)

# 150 Years of British Steam Locomotives

## Brian Reed

David & Charles
Newton Abbot    London
North Pomfret (VT)    Vancouver

ISBN 0 7153 7051 0
Library of Congress Catalog Card Number 75 – 10514

© Brian Reed 1975

Set in 10 on 11pt Plantin
and printed in Great Britain
by Redwood Burn Limited, Trowbridge & Esher
for David & Charles (Holdings) Limited
South Devon House   Newton Abbot   Devon

Published in the United States of America
by David & Charles Inc
North Pomfret   Vermont 05053   USA

Published in Canada
by Douglas David & Charles Limited
132 Philip Avenue   North Vancouver   BC

# Contents

# 1 Some Fundamentals

Apart from the first four of all, steam locomotives from the beginning in 1803 to the end of new construction for Britain in 1960 were pre-eminently creatures of their environment. Constant reference back to this cliché explains many restrictions, many novelties, and the actual trend of development and construction at different periods, which were governed more by manufacturing and mechanical engineering possibilities, and by the vagaries and uncertainties of financial-economic practices, than by true railway requirements.

Throughout the whole period locomotive design, construction and operation in Britain were more of an art than a science. Some consummate artists came forth; many were scarcely pavement artists. At the beginning a different situation was hardly possible; yet even in the 20th century scientific thought developed from fundamentals was scantily applied, and personal preferences based on incomplete thinking and pure emotion were prevalent, so that in the end the results fell short of what might reasonably have been expected from 150 years of development and the immense range of resources and facilities available to a nationalised railway system from a whole nation.

Only development of early primitive steam locomotives permitted the transmutation of the old waggonways, tramways and rail-roads into a country-wide railway system. Having brought something greater than itself, the steam locomotive, or rather the locomotive engineers, continued to control development and operation much as in later years holders of £10,000 worth of founders' shares controlled £10 million commercial enterprises. Often they restricted changes to more suitable methods in the fashion of a debenture-holders' committee. Little basic adaptation of steam power to suit widening railway requirements was made, and gradually railway systems in fully-developed countries became unbalanced, financially and technically.

Financial unbalance came from the general monetary system that did not, and does not, permit the automatic elimination or costless writing off of capital when the physical items it represents are no longer in existence. Within the capital structure of British Railways on its formation in 1948 was the legacy of Stockton & Darlington Railway capital of 1820-30, when nothing was left to represent it other than *Locomotion* on its plinth at Darlington station and a few small exhibits in York railway museum.

Two locomotive causes substantially helped the technical unbalance of railways in Britain and other highly developed countries, though they became of major importance only during this century, and then to increasing tempo. First, the continued construction of conventional steam locomotives of ever-increasing size and weight perpetuated low power : weight ratios against total moving weight when, conversely, ever higher speeds and increasing density of traffic were calling for just the opposite. Such matters were not of such moment in George Stephenson's day; they became decisive during the 20th Century.

With conventional steam locomotives high power : weight ratios could be provided only with inconvenience. For example, 160 tons of locomotive and tender weight and an axle load of 22 tons were required on the LNER to maintain a 70mph schedule over a level route with the 240-ton Silver Jubilee. Low power weight ratios promoted potentialities for unpunctual working; but for many years only in Britain was this supplemented by that far greater promoter of unpunctuality – the unbraked freight train.

Secondly, continued development of reciprocating steam locomotives forming no more than five to eight per cent of the wheeled stock of a railway gradually dictated the use of rails twice as heavy and bridges twice as strong as those needed by the other 92-95 per cent of the wheeled stock. This could not be called efficient or economic; but no attempts were made to develop high tractive effort, acceptable speed and great horsepower on axle loads low enough for substantial savings to be made in track cost and bridge construction. By the time the Garratt locomotive was well developed only railways 'up country', or those with exceptional drawgear, could derive proper benefit from it. Apart from a few examples in North America from World War I years, not until the 1950s was deliberate application made of wagons with laden axle loads equal to those of the locomotives that handled them. This unbalance was aggravated in Britain by the perpetuation of three-link loose couplings and unbraked freight trains.

The dominant position, and even more the restricted capacities, of the locomotive engineer were accentuated also by the 'vested interests' that grew up in the British railway world and prevented free interchange and common cause, and admitted no new ideas from outside, taking only those that arose inside the particular closed ring. This was one major reason for what may not unjustly be called the great brake scandal. These factors remained almost unabated to the end of steam. The operation and operating ratios of British Railways since 1

January 1948 have been shaped greatly by the locomotive engineer and his limitations, which have prevented successful adaptation to rapidly changing conditions; and the huge 'paper' losses have been shaped by continuance of financial pundits equally unable to adjust themselves to the times.

One might well ask how a seemingly crude and ineffective machine could gain, and retain long after its day, the enormous interest, and even affection, given to the steam reciprocating locomotive. Possibly the reason is because of all man's engineering productions the steam locomotive is likest unto man — and woman. Within the large general framework of environment it showed the same immense range of capacity and characteristics; it was almost unpredictable in its performance except in large generalised terms; its day to day performance was affected profoundly by its physical condition; it had every shape, size, formation, colour defect and protruberance (warts and all), and almost every human characteristic from gentleness and urbanity to viciousness and irresponsibility; it proceeded with gaits that varied from the smooth and dignified to the rolling and unsteady; it could often limp or stagger home unassisted after misfortunes or spew-out of potations that had been too deep; and, as one of the kindliest presidents of the Institution of Mechanical Engineers once remarked, it was human in being easy and delightful to conceive but painful and difficult to deliver.

Governing condition for all steam locomotives was the ferrous wheel on the ferrous rail. The only change in these frictional conditions from the time of Trevithick was the machining of the wheel tread and the smoother rail head. The effect of this was marginal, as was the effect of multi-cylinder propulsion. The only attempt at modification on any serious scale was the rack railway, for the application of rubber tyres did not get beyond railcars. Limitations of the steel wheel on the steel rail acted equally in traction and retardation, and as the railway system matured, braking became at least as important as tractive effort and horsepower. To this day the need for friction to give high accelerative and decelerative performances has to be carefully balanced against the need to reduce friction to give low resistance to movement and reduce the needed power output.

Effectiveness of the steam reciprocating locomotive arose primarily from the direct drive between piston and wheel tread, by which the starting of the prime mover meant automatically the starting of the locomotive and its train. In this it differed from the internal-combustion engine, and much effort in the early days of diesel traction was devoted to attempts to reproduce the direct-drive effect of the steam locomotive.

Moreover, the commercial effectiveness of the steam reciprocating locomotive depended on less than half a dozen essentials. They were: (1) two or more cylinders with cranks at different angles to ensure starting in any position and give reasonably constant torque; (2) the multitubular fire-tube boiler to ensure adequate steam generation within permissible weight and size limits; (3) the blast pipe, which was necessary to get the potential generating capacity out of the multitubular boiler, and to give automatic regulation of the steam-generating and steam-utilising portions of the whole machine; and (4) expansion valve motion to give fuel economy and permit high speed. Compounding was no more than an extension of the expansion principles, though its practical advantages were in other ways. Within the present century came the addition of something fundamental in a thermodynamic sense — the superheater. It was essential only in permitting further enhancement of power and giving additional fuel economy.

The probable adequacy of the relatively smooth iron wheel on the relatively smooth iron rail for light loads was shown by Trevithick's locomotives, and three of these also included blast-pipe exhaust. In 1812 came the first application of two cylinders at right angles; but not until 1829 were more than two of the four essentials embodied in any one locomotive, and as a result the steam locomotive then made a sudden bound forward. Only in 1829-31 did the steam locomotive take on the basic form it maintained for the next 130 years, and justified the term, often used up to the end, of the 'Stephenson' locomotive. That term denoted Robert at least as much as George.

# 2 From Trevithick to Stephenson

Practical measures for locomotives came first with Richard Trevithick's high-pressure stationary engines evolved 1799-1801, though before that some possibilities of travelling engines on Watt's low-pressure system seem to have been mooted,[1] and road locomotives on other systems had been tried experimentally by Cugnot (1769) and Murdoch (1784).

Conviviality ended Trevithick's own first road locomotive attempt in 1801, but the results were good enough for money to be found to get Trevithick from Cornwall to London and pay fees for a patent[2] to cover high-pressure, or 'strong steam', engines as such and the application thereof to road and rail vehicles. The patent specification stated that in general the ordinary surface of the wheel would be sufficient for adhesion. No mention was made of blast pipe or any other kind of exhaust; but a claim was made for two cylinders with cranks at right angles.

Matthew Murray usually has been given the credit of initiating cranks at right angles in his patent,[3] perhaps because all Trevithick's locomotives had single cylinders, whereas Murray applied twin cylinders and cranks at 90° to the first locomotives he built, though that was not until 1812. The Trevithick patent also covered mechanically-driven pump feed to the boiler, feedwater heating, and boiler lagging by exhaust steam.

Trevithick was responsible for four locomotives: (1) the Coalbrookdale locomotive 1803: (2) the Penydarren engine 1804; (3) the Gateshead engine 1805; and (4) the London locomotive 1808.

Construction of (1) was undertaken by the customer, the Coalbrookdale Ironworks in Shropshire, a firm with long experience in tramway and waggonway materials and general ironwork, and noted for its cast iron cylinders for steam engines. For well over a century the actual completion of this locomotive was scarcely appreciated, and the drawing found later was thought to be that of Trevithick's next locomotive. Only on discovery that the Coalbrookdale way had been narrowed to a gauge of about 3ft and converted from an edge way to a tramway prior to 1800 came the realisation that this drawing represented the first locomotive of all.

Engine (2) was the most famous of the four, largely because it won a bet of 500 guineas for Samual Homfray, the ironmaster owning the Penydarren works near Dowlais, South Wales, where the locomotive was built under the supervision of Trevithick. It is the only one of the four of which no pictorial representation exists; all that is known about it is contained in letters of Trevithick and Homfray.[4] Between February and July 1804 it ran some trips over the 9½-mile tramway from the works to the Glamorganshire canal, but broke too many of the thin angled tram plates, and was dismantled and parts used for works purposes.

No 3 was built at the Gateshead works of John Whinfield, the Trevithick agent for high-pressure engines in the north-east, to the requirements of Christopher Blackett, proprietor of the Wylam waggonway. Though completed and put through a few runs in the works yard it was not accepted, possibly because on completion Blackett realised its weight of 4½ to 5 tons on four wheels with a tread width of 1in was impracticable for the wooden edge rails with which the Wylam line was laid. It was the first locomotive to be built with flanged wheels.

All three had a single horizontal cylinder inserted in the boiler end, a wide transverse crosshead encircling two cylindrical guide bars, gear drive, and a big flywheel to get the engine over dead centres on stationary duties. As in waggon practice of the time, the wheels were loose on the axles; and as the gears were on one side only, though there was a crank at each side, the drive was only on to the two left-hand wheels. Thus the adhesion weight was only half the locomotive weight, and there was a strong shouldering couple that forced the driving wheels against the sides of the rail.

The Coalbrookdale boiler had two internal flues of different diameters, connected externally at the end remote from the chimney; succeeding Trevithick engines, to gauges above 4ft, had rather larger diameter boilers in which a wholly internal return flue could be incorporated. Machinery arrangements of No 1 must have been dictated largely by the narrow gauge. In No 3, and possibly in No 2, the whole layout was reversed, the cylinder being at the end opposite to the chimney and firehole, and the crankshaft located between chimney and boiler end. Layout of the Penydarren engine is not known, but as the gauge was 4ft 2in between backs of tram plates it may well have been like that of the Gateshead engine.

No information exists as to how the exhaust steam was led to atmosphere in No 1, but Trevithick's letters show that the exhaust of No 2 was up the chimney and that he was beginning to appreciate the value of this. How the engine ran from Penydarren to the canal wharf is unknown, for there was a tunnel en route that was lower than the height of the chimney.

No safety valve seems to have been fitted to any Trevithick locomotive, but No 2 is recorded by Trevithick to have had a lead rivet in the flue top and this acted as a fusible plug – the first one known. Two, if not three, of the locomotives were multi-purpose machines to do both stationary and traction work and had a form of clutch to disengage the drive from the rail wheels when not on the tramway.

In all three locomotives the cast iron boiler acted as the frame, and to it were attached cylinder, crankshaft bearings, the bearings for intermediate gear wheels, axle supports, and whatever drawgear there was. Despite the provisions of the 1802 patent not one of these locomotives had pump or any other feed to the boiler, and once the contents were consumed the boiler had to be refilled by hand.

Trevithick's fourth locomotive differed from the others in having a single vertical cylinder inserted in the boiler top at the back end, and it had direct drive down to crankpins in the rear wheels. It was the first direct-drive locomotive, the first single driver, the first 2-2-0, and the first passenger engine, and an express passenger engine at that, for speeds up to 20mph were contemplated, though probably not reached. It ran on a circular track within an enclosure on the site of the present University of London buildings at various times between July and September 1808; and in view of the speed and proposals for several hours of continuous running it was the first locomotive to have a footplate.

This engine was built complete to Trevithick's requirements by Hazeldine & Co of Bridgnorth, then under the technical leadership of John Urpeth Rastrick. Known as *Catch me who can*, it ran on tram rails laid on continuous baulks of wood. No dimensions other than its weight are on record, and nothing is known as to its fate. As with No 2 it was connected with a bet, Trevithick offering to back it to make a greater mileage in 24 hr than any horse in England.

Trevithick's locomotives were before their time; there was no pressing economic or engineering need for any of them. Not one did useful or concentrated work yet they were not without influence on later practice. All four operated with the adhesion from normal treads on normal rails or tramplates; but with only half the locomotive weight adhesive they did not prove the adequacy of the smooth wheel on the smooth rail for economic haulage, and the doubts that arose led to the peculiar form of the first post-Trevithick type, which was intended to do a job of work and to counter the increasing cost of horse traction (up to £80 a year 'working' expenses per horse) due to the long-continued Napoleonic wars.

This first commercial application of steam traction was the Blenkinsop type working from Middleton colliery to Leeds, about 2½ miles. From the beginning loads above 10 times the locomotive weight were hauled along the level. Consideration of loads such as these led Blenkinsop to make certain of daily operation by using a rack.

Blenkinsop's patent[5] was for a railway system, not a locomotive, but he did 'declare that a steam engine is greatly to be preferred to any other first mover'. More than any other man of his time who was in a position to have locomotives built, Blenkinsop realised the possibility of immediate applications to lines other than his own. Over the next few years, while retaining his position as Charles Brandling's manager and partner at Middleton, he did intensive sales work in the north of England, and by 1816 more than half of all steam locomotives at work were of his type.

Design and construction of the locomotives were left to Matthew Murray of the firm of Fenton, Murray & Wood at Leeds (price £350 to £400 each), and the Middleton way was relaid with cast iron edge rails, one of which had semi-circular cogs on the side which meshed with the final gear wheel on the locomotive. The four road wheels were flanged. Blenkinsop paid the Trevithick patent-holders £30 a locomotive licence fee for the use of the high-pressure principles, and this would be the reason for the use of Trevithick's four-way plug-type valves for the cylinders in preference to Murray's own short flat-D outside-admission slide valves.

The distinct advance of the Blenkinsop-Murray locomotives was the use of two cylinders with cranks at right angles. The exhaust did not go up the chimney and so did not influence the fire, though the boiler was only a single-flue type and so had not the potential evaporative capacity of the Trevithick return-flue form. Cast iron was still the boiler material, but the shell was oval, possibly to accommodate both the vertical cylinders plus a 14in flue. No means of boiler feed were fitted at first, so again the work done was limited to one boiler filling, which lasted about five miles. Blenkinsop had a scheme for filling against pressure from a high water tower, but this was not put into effect. Recorded pressure was 50-55psi. A defect was the rack on one side only, which gave a twisting effect against the rails, but it was retained on the grounds of simplicity and expense though the patent covered a rack on each side. A central rack would have prevented horse traction, which was used on the Middleton way and other lines where racks were put down whenever the locomotives had to be laid off.

The first locomotive was ready and tried in June 1812; it and a second one were put to regular work in August that year. The two vertical cylinders were let into the boiler, with the valve gear and an open exhaust outlet between them, and they drove separate intermediate shafts through the connecting rods. Gear wheels on these shafts engaged with a central gear below the boiler, and on the left-hand side of that shaft was the large toothed wheel that meshed with the rack. An advance on Trevithick practice was a separate wooden frame that carried the boiler through four fixed brackets on the upper side and the four axle bearings on the under side.

Two more locomotives of the same type were built for Middleton in 1813 and worked another section. From 1814 eccentric drives to the valves and wrought iron boilers with return flues were adopted gradually, and by 1815 all Leeds-built engines had been given a silencer box between cylinders and final exhaust, a spring-loaded safety valve, and a mechanically-driven boiler feed pump that lifted water from a frame-mounted tank at the back end. Engine weight at first was about 5 tons but the Middleton engines themselves in after years scaled $6\frac{1}{4}$ tons. From earliest days trailing loads of 70 to 85 tons could be drawn along the level, and later records show up to 140 tons, or 24 times the locomotive weight. Such loads justified the cost of the rack for they were far above the possibilities of plain adhesion wheels on the light tracks at that time.

By 1816 at least six Blenkinsop rack locomotives were or had been at work at Kenton & Coxlodge colliery (Newcastle), Willington (Tyneside), Orrell (Wigan) and Whitehaven, and two had been built in Germany. Those at Wigan and Whitehaven were built locally; those in the north-east were made by Murray, and the two for Newcastle in 1813-14 show the first known attempt at standardisation of parts, for on 14 October 1814 Murray wrote to Watson, who was handling the business: 'In your new engines we will endeavour to make the four cylinders one exact size, you can then have a pair of spare pistons to fit either engine.'[6]

All engines except the German pair did useful work over some years. Pronounced drop in the price of horse fodder, and the remaining locomotive being almost worn out, led to steam traction being given up entirely at Middleton in 1835 after a period of growing horse traction when, according to a table published in 1837, the average trailing load of a locomotive was only 33 tons. This change is not surprising, for according to the investigations of Rastrick and Walker for the Liverpool & Manchester Railway, the coal consumption was enormous at $2\frac{3}{4}$lb/ton-mile.

The commercial success of the Middleton locomotives involved additional capital investment of around £700 a mile for the rack rails, which might be warranted for a considerable daily tonnage, but for other routes two questions were still unanswered: (1) what *was* the effective adhesion between a smooth iron rail and smooth iron wheel?, and (2) was it possible to devise a machine to take advantage of that adhesion usefully and which would suit the light edge rails and tramplates then prevalent? The two men who set out in 1812 to solve these questions were William Chapman and William Hedley, who, though working separately, must have had some interchange of ideas.

Chapman began in 1813 with a locomotive built for him probably by the Butterley Iron Co, which pulled itself along a chain or rope laid between the wooden rails of the Heaton waggonway at Newcastle. As far as is known it had four wheels, and two vertical cylinders sunk within the boiler which drove the chain rollers by side lever mechanism and a two-speed gear. A more important part of Chapman's 1812 patent[7] was that covering the equalisation of the load on the road wheels of springless six- and eight-wheel locomotives and to enable them to pass round curves, for Chapman was convinced that such multi-axle types were needed to get adequate traction capacity on the existing light rails. This led to the first bogie locomotive, an eight-wheeler arranged in two trucks which gave longitudinal but not transverse equalisation, and which was built for Chapman by Phineas Crowther of Newcastle.

This locomotive was set to work on the Lambton waggonway in Co Durham in December 1814 and a contemporary description includes the first record of locomotive driving wheels slipping under high tractive effort. It was the first locomotive with two cranks at right angles on the same shaft, and as such was a further small step towards what became eventually the conventional direct drive. Chapman's first locomotive did not last long in chain form, but seems to have been rebuilt as a six-wheel adhesion locomotive with two of the axles arranged in a bogie, and in that form worked for some years into the 1820s at Heaton, but not with a long haul at first as much of the Heaton waggonway continued with wooden rails until 1821.

In 1808 the Wylam line was relaid with cast iron tramplates to a gauge equivalent to 5ft to replace the wooden rails that had precluded the trial of the Trevithick-Whinfield locomotive in 1805, and in 1812 Blackett sanctioned the construction of a locomotive. Years later William Hedley claimed that as viewer, or manager, at Wylam he began experiments in October 1812 with a hand-operated vehicle which had satisfied him as to the efficacy of normal adhesion and which settled that question generally. Nevertheless, his patent of 1813[8] deals almost entirely with means of increasing friction such as teeth and flanges, and apart from that it really covers nothing at all.

Wylam *Puffing Billy* of 1815 as it was around 1864;
the two sons of William Hedley alongside to left.

The first locomotive to run at Wylam was a
single-cylinder Trevithick type built in 1813 by
Thomas Waters of Gateshead, who by then was the
north-eastern agent for Trevithick-type engines
generally. It had gear drive, flywheel and a
single-flue boiler, and was the first Trevithick-type
locomotive to do useful work, for it was in operation, at least intermittently, for a year or so.
Presumably it had exhaust blast up the chimney; if
so, the Wylam people did not see the advantage.

During its operation a two-cylinder four-wheel
locomotive later to be known as *Puffing Billy* was
put in hand at Wylam. This locomotive was completed around March 1814, and soon after was
supplemented by a generally similar unit now
known as *Wylam Dilly*. A third was built subsequently. Possibly *Puffing Billy* was the first
locomotive to have a wrought iron boiler and the
first to have cylinders outside the boiler. Corresponding with the facilities at the Wylam shops the
cylinders were of plate, and though at first they
were lagged with wood they seem to have been un-
lagged in later years. At first the exhaust went
straight from cylinder to atmosphere; after a short

time a silencer or exhaust box was inserted and the
outflow from that taken to the chimney.

From the beginning these 5-ton locomotives broke
too many tramplates, and during 1815 they were
rebuilt as eight-wheelers. The illustration often
reproduced since 1825[9] has purported to show the
Wylam locomotives in their eight-wheel form, but is
almost certainly Chapman's drawing of his own
eight-wheel double-bogie Lambton engine. The
Wylam locomotives must have been rebuilt on
Chapman's principles, though neither Hedley nor
his family in later years gave Chapman any credit.

In 1828 the Wylam way was again relaid, and in
the process was reconverted from a tramway to a
railway with edge rails of cast iron. The
eight-wheelers were then converted back to
four-wheelers, but other substantial modifications
were made coincidently, additional to the provision
of flanged wheels. In this revised form two
locomotives worked intermittently until about 1862,
when they were held for preservation; one is now in
the Science Museum at South Kensington and the
other in the Royal Scottish Museum in Edinburgh.

The one thing definitely known about performance at Wylam is contained in Timothy
Hackworth's notebook[10] under date August 1828.
From this it appears that one eight-wheel
locomotive could handle about 10,000 chaldrons a

Killingworth locomotive rebuilt with new wheels and other parts, as it stood for many years on the High Level bridge, Newcastle.

year in 820 journeys at a total cost of £372, and that all the gear wheels and half the road wheels normally needed renewal within the year.

George Stephenson first appeared on the locomotive scene at the time Chapman's and Hedley's two-cylinder locomotives were coming on to the rails. He began to build his first locomotive *Blucher* in the autumn of 1813 at Killingworth and it was in steam at the end of July 1814. Therefore he could have had little of that help from visits to Wylam always claimed by protagonists of Hedley and Hackworth, for in 1813 all Wylam had running was the single-cylinder Trevithick-type locomotive, and *Puffing Billy* was on the rails only some four months before *Blucher*. His useful pre-knowledge must have been gained from inspections of the Blenkinsop rack locomotives on the Kenton-Coxlodge and Willington waggonways, and perhaps because of this his initial locomotive does not seem to have had blast-pipe exhaust when built. Writing in 1830 Robert Stephenson and Joseph Locke recorded:[11] 'This [augmenting of fire temperature] was affected shortly after the first Locomotive Engine was tried on the Killingworth Railway by conveying the steam to the chimney where it escaped in a perpendicular direction up the centre.'

*Blucher* was the first flanged wheel adhesion locomotive to do any work; otherwise it was not of very notable design, and had Murray's type of drive to two gear shafts with cranks at right angles, from which further gears led to two axles in place of Blenkinsop's rack drive. The boiler was of single-flue type. Apparently there was a water chamber round the chimney that acted as a feedwater heater, and from which a mechanically-driven feed pump drew the water for the boiler. According to Nicholas Wood it also had a chain drive from one axle to the axle of the tender or convoy carriage to gain extra adhesion weight. This engine pulled six times its own weight up 1 in 450, but was recorded to be very noisy and rough, as would be the Blenkinsop, Chapman and Hedley locomotives.

How slow, cautious and uncertain were the steps from Trevithick's first locomotive to the later conventional steam locomotive drive is shown by Stephenson's second locomotive, completed in March 1815, which incorporated improvements outlined in his joint patent of that year.[12] Though the patent included the driven tender the mechanism was not applied, as experience with *Blucher* had shown it was not worthwhile. The distinct mechanical advance was the deliberate elimination of gear drive and rack rails and the substitution of two vertical cylinders driving down direct to crankpins in the wheels; the pins in one wheel-and-axle group were at right angles to those in the other group. Thus the unpatented direct drive of Trevithick's *Catch me who can* was resuscitated, but this time in a coupled locomotive with cranks at right angles.

To couple the two axles the patent named alternatives of inside sprockets and chains or inside cranks and coupling rods. Which was used in this second locomotive is uncertain, though chains seem probable and were used in later Killingworth locomotives. A separate frame supported the boiler and took the axle bearings and drawgear, and along this frame the leading axle bearings could be adjusted slightly to take up chain stretch. This meant the cylinder line was then not on the bearing and axle line.

An increase in flue diameter raised the evaporative capacity; as a result, according to Wood, the blast exhaust was not always considered essential, and at one time some of the later Killingworth engines seem to have worked temporarily without it. Nor did all Killingworth locomotives retain pump feed, and as late as January 1825 a demonstration given to committees of the Liverpool & Manchester and Birmingham-Liverpool Railways had to be limited to 14 miles when the boiler had to be refilled with 200gal of fresh warm water, probably by a hand pump.

All questions of adhesion and of the evaporative capacity of single-flue boilers down to after the time of the first public railway to be worked by steam were at their simplest, because every railway or tramway to which locomotives were applied had a down grade in favour of the load. Thus steam traction was established under conditions that were easiest for it.

Another Stephenson joint patent of 1816[13] included strengthened cast iron wheels, the application of separate tyres shrunk on, and the well-known steam springs. These were intended primarily as weight equalisers on four- and six-wheel locomotives, and were Stephenson's version of the Chapman ideas. Initial application was to the centre axle only of the first six-wheeler, the chain-coupled 0-6-0 of the Kilmarnock & Troon Railway in 1816. The longitudinal adjustment could not be repeated where steam springs were used on more than one axle, as they were on some of the subsequent Killingworth four-wheelers, but with the coming of acceptable plate springs from around 1822 they were gradually given up for new construction.

Stephenson built only four or five locomotives for Killingworth over the years 1814-21 with successive detail improvements. Another five to the same general design were supplied to Hetton colliery in 1822. No authentic record of the builder of these five remains; probably parts were supplied by Killingworth and by Burrell in Newcastle, and erection done on site. Hetton was a new pit opened in 1822, and the two nearly level sections of its railway route down to the River Wear formed the first railway to be built specifically for operation by steam locomotives.

The Stephenson engines just detailed established the 'Killingworth type', and more appear to have been built at that place by Nicholas Wood. They had the characteristics of two vertical cylinders let into the boiler, direct drive to crankpins in the wheels, coupling of the two axles by internal chains, and single-flue boilers. In general the cylinders were about 9in bore, of cast iron lined with copper sheet, and with valves operated at first by a tumbler, though later Wood introduced loose eccentric actuation. Some time after 1825 outside coupling rods were adopted for new Killingworth engines and are believed to have been applied to some of the older engines in place of the chains, though chains were still in use at various places in 1827.

According to J. Adamson's Book[14] the performance of a Killingworth locomotive was '126,000 tons conveyed one mile in 312 days. The performance at the Hetton colliery during the same period amounted to 198,000 tons conveyed one mile. The difference arises from the greater regularity of the line in the latter case.' Adamson also records the first suggestion for banking power: 'The use of two engines on such slopes, one acting in front of a train of waggons and the other behind them, has been proposed by Mr Stephenson of Newcastle upon Tyne, and where the inclinations are of considerable length, would form a most convenient method of surmounting them.'

George Dodds on the Monkland & Kirkintilloch Railway in 1831 resuscitated the Killingworth type with outside coupling rods and other improvements including one not initiated at Killingworth: a flue furnace with a few small tubes from the front tube plate to the chimney base; there was no separate smokebox. The two Monkland locomotives were the first built in Scotland other than Timothy Burstall's *Perseverance* entered at Rainhill in 1829, and were constructed by Murdoch & Aitken in Glasgow.

George Stephenson's greatest claim in regard to locomotives as distinct from railways is that from 1815 to 1825 no steam locomotives other than by him were built in Britain. Moreover, he continued those 10 years in growing faith in the steam locomotive as the motive power of the future and urged it whenever he could, as at Darlington from

1821, through a time when every one else had given it up for new construction. At the same time he made but trifling improvements in the locomotive itself and permitted what was even a deterioration in design just when an improvement was needed most decisively.

He was not the father of the locomotive; he contributed few salient developments, and was never responsible himself for any really noteworthy design, though he held back more than one promising development through caution and obstinacy. From his appointment as engineer of the Stockton & Darlington he began gradually to visualise a country-wide system of railways to one rail gauge with steam locomotives as the motive power and, apart from very steep grades, rejected the central power plant as represented by cable haulage and self-acting inclines.

When Stephenson went to Killingworth the waggonway had been in operation some 40 years to a gauge of 4ft 8in. It was not altered, but when Stephenson grew beyond Killingworth and engineered the Hetton and Springwell ways, the SDR, the Bolton & Leigh and the Liverpool & Manchester, he merely kept the gauge to which he was accustomed. As M. J. T. Lewis put it succinctly:[15] 'If Stephenson had found his mission in life at Heaton, our standard gauge would probably be 4ft 3in; if at Wylam, about 5ft. It was largely a question of chance.'

# 3   The Stockton & Darlington Phase

By the opening day (27 September 1825) of the first public railway to be operated by steam traction (the Stockton & Darlington Railway, or SDR) at least 30 steam locomotives had been built in England and one in Wales. Between them they had shown non-rack types to give sufficient adhesion to haul economic loads up grades of 1 in 100/115 or flatter; they had shown two cylinders with cranks at right angles to be essential; they included the first five bogie locomotives; the desirability of the blast pipe for single- and return-flue boilers had been demonstrated; the cast iron boiler shell had given way to multi-plate malleable iron construction; spring-loaded safety valves had been introduced; and other details tried or established were direct drive, mechanical pump feed, fusible plugs, feedwater heating, steam jacketing of cylinders (by the boiler), slide valves, and eccentric actuation of valve movment. All two-cylinder locomotives had vertical cylinders and 25 of the 30 locomotives had cylinders inserted in the boiler.

The recognised importance of the SDR as a test case for public railways and for steam traction might have been expected to bring some distinct advance in locomotive type. In fact, the only locomotive ready by opening day was of cruder design and rougher construction than a Killingworth engine. The second, delivered in November 1825, was even less satisfactory, and Nos

*Locomotion* that opened the Stockton & Darlington Railway in September 1825 and still preserved at Darlington.

3 and 4 delivered in the spring of 1826 were little better — all this despite manufacture at the one works established particularly for locomotive building.

Appreciating the coming advance in railways and locomotives, George Stephenson in June 1823 joined with his son Robert, Michael Longridge, and the Darlington Quaker Edward Pease to form the firm of Robert Stephenson & Co, and a small factory was opened at Newcastle upon Tyne to build locomotives and other engines, and do general engineering work. At first young Robert Stephenson (1803-59) managed the works, but in June 1824 he departed for the mines in South America and did not return to England until the end of 1827. Old George was fully occupied in the construction of the SDR, in dealing with the surveys and business of the first and unsuccessful LMR Bill, and in other projects, and rarely was active in the works. He was not even a financial partner between 1825 and 1841, though he continued in authority whenever he chose to exert it. Pease, a leading figure in the SDR until 1826, had put up 40 per cent of the money and at 60 years of age did not wish to engage in management affairs. Longridge had his own ironworks 12 miles away at Bedlington to occupy his attention.

Thus there was no direction of the works after Robert's departure until Longridge unwillingly took the management in January 1825 while retaining the necessary oversight of his own works. Much later claims of the Hackworth family that Timothy had been manager at the Forth Street works in 1824 are to be discounted; there is no direct evidence of this. James Kennedy, later a partner in Bury, Curtis

& Kennedy in Liverpool, was at the works for some time, though there is no evidence that he had any of the managerial responsibility claimed in his obituary notices many years later.

This lack of competent direction probably was the cause of the first SDR locomotive's cumbrous design and rough workmanship, and for the adoption of the Fremantle grasshopper beam motion for the drive in place of the simpler Killingworth crosshead and slidebar type, and also for the change in slide valve actuation.[16] SDR No 1 (later *Locomotion* – SDR locomotive names were added later) was the first railway engine to have the drive for two slide valves at different phases taken off one eccentric, and is the first known definitely to have had lap and lead, though the proportions of the lead were different in front and back cylinders. Outside coupling rods were used, and again this is the first known adoption. As back and front drives were at 90°, one flycrank connection and one direct pin connection had to be provided on each side.

The outside coupling rod connection might have been due to one axle of *Locomotion* being contained in a transverse tube pivoted at the centre in a bracket below the boiler. This gave three-point support to the springless four-wheel locomotive, and was another attempt to give the equalising effect on rough tracks sought first by Chapman in 1812; but it made the Killingworth inside chain coupling impossible. According to Marc Seguin's notes of December 1825[17] and the Prussian observers von Dechen and von Oeyenhausen in 1827,[18] some of the SDR four-wheelers had both axles running in tubes, though only one was centrally pivoted. Such an arrangement meant a change in valve motion from *Locomotion*, for an inside eccentric could not be mounted. Thus SDR Nos 2-4 had a valve drive taken from the centre of one coupling rod to an eccentric shaft above the boiler, and on which were mounted two eccentrics, one for each cylinder.

*Locomotion* had been running scarcely three months when there appeared on the SDR the most remarkable locomotive of its time: Robert Wilson's four-wheel four-cylinder locomotive sent from Newcastle on a month's trial, price to be £380 if bought. The cylinders were vertical, grouped two on each side outside the boiler, and the two piston rods were yoked to a common return connecting rod which drove down on to a crankpin in the hind wheel. The two groups were at 90° to each other, and the wheels were coupled by outside rods. Piston valves were actuated by cranks and eccentrics from the crankpins of the rear wheels, and form the first known application of such valves, though no details of construction exist. The only known illustration of Wilson's product is the sketch made from the locomotive itself by Marc Seguin in December 1825,

and this shows also the one feature adopted in later practice, the two-piece cast iron plug wheels evolved by Wilson in an attempt to strengthen considerably the old Killingworth wheel with eight cast or malleable spokes, and yet keep within the casting and machining possibilities of the time and provide a renewable wearing portion. Wilson's engine seems to have run only through December 1825 and was then laid aside on the SDR, though remaining Wilson's property until April 1827 when the SDR bought it for £160 for the sake of its boiler.

Hackworth adopted the Wilson wheel for SDR locomotives, but he was not the inventor of it as claimed later by his family. Such wheels were supplied from Stephenson's works as SDR replacements from 1826, though then and for eight or nine years thereafter a few SDR engines continued with wooden wheels, so the two-piece plug type was not the final answer, though it continued in new construction until 1846-48 and can still be seen in *Locomotion* and the 0-6-0 *Derwent* preserved at Darlington.

A separate malleable iron tyre shrunk on to a cast iron centre had been part of the Losh and Stephenson patent of 1816; it was not applied to the first half-dozen or so SDR engines as built, but had been adopted by 1829 and is shown first in Rastrick's sketch of *Royal George* made in January of that year[19] and in the form proposed in 1816, that is with the flange as part of the cast iron rim. Similar tyres but with integral flanges were attached also to wooden wheel centres, as were cast iron tyres, and of the latter Rastrick recorded they lasted only 10 weeks on wooden wheels.

Next unusual SDR engine was a Stephenson four-wheeler received in November 1827, which after desultory and unsatisfactory performance was laid off in March 1828. In July an order for rebuilding into a six-wheeler with springs was given to Stephenson; the new frame and extra wheels were sent from Forth Street and re-erection done by Stephenson men in the SDR shops. By October the rebuild was giving such satisfaction that Hackworth was instructed to put springs on all engines as soon as possible. This could not be done throughout the stock, as engines with vertical cylinders above the driving wheels could not take them because of piston clearance.

Eventually named *Experiment*, this locomotive was notable as being the first two-cylinder locomotive with horizontal cylinders, but they were inserted high up in the rear end of the boiler, and the piston rods drove the connecting rods through an arrangement of pivoted oscillating levers, hence its general name of the Lever or Quadrant engine. This arrangement was retained in the rebuild but the connecting rods were greatly lengthened to drive

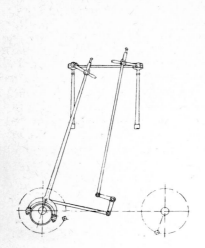
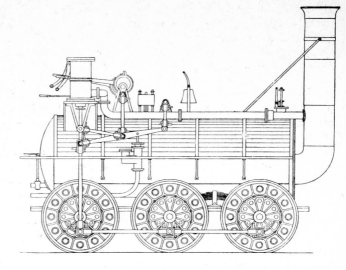

Fig 1
Left: Eccentric actuation of *Locomotion*'s two slide valves, 1825
Right: Hackworth's *Royal George* of the SDR built 1827; as running in 1829

on to the leading coupled wheels. J. U. Rastrick examined the rebuild in January 1829 when making investigations as to possible traction methods for the Liverpool & Manchester Railway (LMR), and the sketch in his notebook is the only record of the appearance of the rebuild. The original boiler had water-tube firebars connected to a forward-running water tube housed in the flue, but the rebuild had a normal single-flue boiler.

Immediatly following the Lever engine came Hackworth's *Royal George,* the first six-wheeler on the SDR. It had been some months under construction at the SDR Shildon works, and to cheapen and facilitate its construction Wilson's four-cylinder engine had been bought. The boiler shell of that engine must have been lengthened, but whether the internal arrangement was perpetuated cannot be stated because the original arrangement is not really known. *Royal George* when completed at Shildon at the end of November 1827 had a return-flue boiler, the first SDR engine to have one, and initiated what came to be a not uncommon SDR practice of twin tenders, one at each end. That at the chimney end carried the coal and the fireman; that at the cylinder end carried the water and driver. Working pressure as set by the lever safety valve was 40psi, but an additional spring safety valve was set to 52psi.

Originally *Royal George* had compensating levers but no springs for the two coupled axles; the driving axle immediately below the cylinders had no suspension of any kind. The slide valves were driven by a short eccentric shaft on the boiler top, which was

driven off the guiding linkage that restrained the piston rod movements, for the engine did not have crosshead and slidebars. Rastrick's sketch of January 1829 is the earliest illustration, but by then the engine had been provided with 4ft two-piece plug wheels, and also with one spring on each side that supported the two coupled axleboxes.

Probably the original wheels were of the malleable iron disc type shown in the model of *Royal George* purchased by the Science Museum in 1898 on the understanding that it had been made by Timothy himself, though the actual work may have been done by Thos Taylor and Wm Sergison, foreman fitter and a turner at Shildon works, under Hackworth's direction. Moreover, in Timothy's own notebook (also at the Science Museum) under date 26 February 1828 is a fully dimensioned drawing of a disc wheel with a note saying, 'two to be made with 10in crank throw and two with 12in', as if trials were to be made with the driving wheels of two further locomotives.

As with all its SDR predecessors *Royal George* had blast-pipe exhaust; nevertheless the chimney, like that of the Lever engine, was carried up 16ft above rail level, so the loading gauge of the SDR was not the beginning of the restricted British loading gauge that has been such a limiting factor for nearly 150 years.

Naturally *Royal George* had about 50 per cent more tractive capacity than the SDR four-wheelers of 1825-28, but the amount of horse-drawn traffic prevented the best being got out of it or of any other locomotive until 1833, and by then it and the older four-wheelers had become engines for secondary haulage by reason of the more powerful 0-6-0s built between 1831 and 1833 under Hackworth's direction. These latter retained vertical cylinders, 14½in by 16in, at one end or the other, though with dummy shaft drive that enabled all of them to be sprung throughout. Those with the cylinders at the chimney end had single-flue boilers, and those with cylinders at the other end had return-flue boilers. In both cases Hackworth had 90 to 100 small tubes put in to finish the gas flow between the end of the flue or return-flue and the smokebox.

These dummy-shaft engines were built in four batches of three, two by Hawthorn and two by Stephenson. The first Hawthorns were the first locomotives built by that firm, whose works were only 200yd west of Stephenson's and had been going since 1817. These slow-speed coal engines are exemplified by *Wilberforce* built in 1833 by Hawthorn, which lasted, though hardly in active service, until the earliest days of photography.

To a small extent the SDR had engines for passenger traffic, known as the coach engines, from 1830, and if they were laid off specific other engines could be inspanned. First of them was the 0-4-0 *Globe* designed by Hackworth and built partly at Stephenson's works and partly at Shildon. It was reminiscent in external appearance of Braithwaite & Ericsson's *William IV* and *Queen Adelaide* for the LMR (1830) and had two inside cylinders low down at the back end driving the front cranked axle. The year 1830 saw also the application of crank axles to Bury's *Liverpool* and the Stephenson-LMR *Planet*. *Globe* at first had water tubes in the main flue, but by 1833 had a main flue, followed by small smoke tubes. It worked until the boiler burst in 1838, after which it was not rebuilt. SDR coach engines burned a mixture of coal and coke.

SDR locomotives continued without stimulus on conservative lines, for speed never was above 15mph and was more generally limited to 6-10mph; but from the beginning of 1828 design at the Newcastle works began gradually to show the effects of the return of Robert Stephenson from South America. He came back still a young man with open mind and progressive ideas and, judging from his own words at later times, with some useful and practical mechanical engineering tenets acquired from Richard Trevithick, whom he had met in Colombia.

Within the 20 months between his return and the completion of *Rocket* in September 1829 the whole administration of the Forth Street (Newcastle) works was tightened up. Robert's mechanical aptitude began to show itself; William Hutchinson was brought forward to take more and more of the daily works management, and one or two definite transitional locomotive designs were built that bridged the gap between the Killingworth and *Locomotion* concepts and *Rocket*. These were principally *Lancashire Witch* and the *Twin Sisters*, the former ordered by the LMR but transferred when built to the Bolton & Leigh Railway.

*Lancashire Witch* did not emanate from Robert in principle, having been conceived by Old George and Henry Booth, treasurer of the LMR, but Robert was back in harness when construction began and he was responsible for design. It was the first deliberate move towards what eventually became the classic steam locomotive horizontal cylinder layout which was visualised as possible by Robert Stephenson immediately after his return, for as early as 1 January 1828 he wrote to Longridge:[20] 'I have been talking a great deal to my father about endeavouring to reduce the size and ugliness of our travelling engines, by applying the engine either on the side of the boiler or beneath it entirely.'

Thus the *Witch* was the first Stephenson locomotive in which the cylinders were removed from the inside of the boiler, and was only the second departure of that maker from the vertical, the 9in by 24in cylinders being supported at a slope of 1:1.3 by plates at the rear end secured to the boiler. *Witch* also had all four axle bearings supported by overhung springs; the 4ft wheels were of wood spread over a base of 5ft.

Being for the LMR, the boiler was designed for coke-burning, whereas all previous locomotives, had burned coal. This led to a remarkable design in which the small central flue containing the grate was divided into two small return flues that came back and joined in the base of a single chimney, and bellows were used to provide forced draught; when examined on the Bolton & Leigh late in 1828 by Coste and Perdonnet it had two straight single flues with a fire in each and the bellows were still being used. More revolutionary was a bevel mechanism that permitted a cut-off around 50 per cent on action by the driver. General performance of the *Witch* early in 1829 was so far in advance of other locomotives that James Walker refused to take it into account when drawing up his report on traction methods for the LMR!

The *Twin Sisters* also had steeply inclined cylinders but was a six-wheeler with wooden wheels and outside coupling rods. It had twin coke-burning vertical boilers built by Laird on Merseyside and sent to Newcastle for erection. Each boiler had its own chimney and they contained the exhaust blasts.

Steeply sloping cylinders were applied by Stephenson also to three other six-wheel locomotives in 1829, one of them being a *Rocket* for the SDR, and No 7 on that line. The other two were for South Wales industrial lines, one being Penydarren. These two probably gave rise to the antiquated style of locomotive evolved by the Neath Abbey Ironworks. The year 1829 was a busy one for the Forth Street works as in addition to the above at least one locomotive was shipped to North America, but everything really culminated in the LMR *Rocket*.

# 4  The Liverpool & Manchester Stage

Progress in the construction of the Liverpool & Manchester by the end of 1828 brought up to high priority the question of motive power, for though George Stephenson, as engineer, had been unwaveringly in support of locomotives he himself had not advanced the locomotive to a point suitable for a passenger-carrying railway, and fixed-engine haulage still had strong support in conservative engineering and business circles. This division of opinion led to the appointment of John Urpeth Rastrick and James Walker to submit reports on the motive power to be adopted from the opening of the line, scheduled for 1830. Walker suggested in February 1829 that a prize be awarded for the best locomotive offered, after its performance had been determined. This was the origin of the Rainhill trials of October 1829, which formed a vital stage in steam locomotive development. In the few brief days

Fig 2
Put forward only as 'a good representation of what *Rocket* was like when first built' by Robert Stephenson & Co in 1929 when making a full size working replica for Henry Ford

of the tests speed came in as a practical commodity.

Yet speed was not the most important stipulation of the competition rules, reflected in the minimum acceptable rate of 10mph. Smokeless combustion was the principal clause, and it was this that resulted in coke being the fuel for the trials, and on the LMR and other railways for many years. Strict limitations of weight and axle load were to be expected, for all parties concerned were troubled by the number of wheel and rail breakages on the SDR and colliery lines with springless locomotives having vertical cylinders. For this reason was added the proviso that engine and boiler must be on springs.

Stipulations approved by the LMR were clear, but no announcement was made as to the exact methods on which the judges would conduct the tests; in fact preliminary trial runs with *Rocket* and *Novelty* had been made before the judges laid down the exact test procedure. Five machines were entered, but actual trials to the specified conditions were made only with *Rocket, Novelty* and *Sans Pareil*. This was a specific competition with stated rules and regulations, and neither the judges nor the

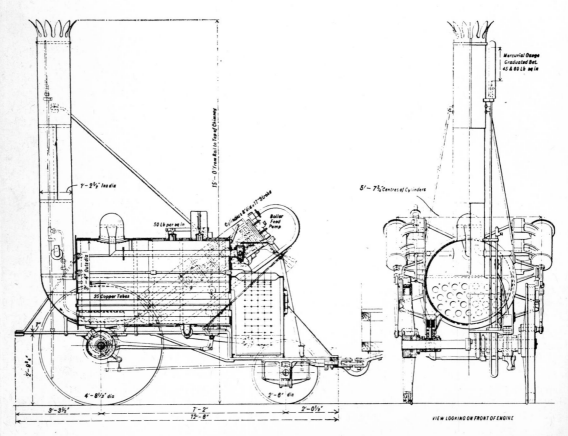

VIEW LOOKING ON FRONT OF ENGINE

LMR were called upon to exercise judgement or discretion, for only one engine fulfilled all conditions and gave the stipulated results.

By good fortune the competition was won by the only locomotive whose principles were straight away capable of the necessary further development. If by some chance *Sans Pareil* had put up a better performance than *Rocket* the judges would have been in a dilemma, for not only did Hackworth fail to comply with the testing rules but his engine was heavier than the prescribed maximum for four wheels. Moreover it did not have springs, and to the springless condition were added vertical cylinders. Any development of these principles was unthinkable, and *Sans Pareil* ideas already were seen to be approaching obsolescence.

*Novelty* was a different proposition altogether. In it the new spirit of speed was given full play, and in its first pre-official run it maintained 28mph for a full mile; but lightness also was a keynote, and that lack of adhesion, plus the boiler type necessary to get it, were not suited for development to the haulage of heavy trains. So easily was this recognised that one admirer in 1830 asked if rack-and-adhesion mechanism could not be put in, a remarkable suggestion for that time. The logical development of *Novelty* would have been 'every vehicle with its own motive power' — admirable if technology in carriage construction had been more advanced, and one that would have brought a railway system different in almost every respect from what did arise.

*Rocket* and the ideas it embodied had greater immediate potentialities than had the other two competitors, and the basic design was capable of substantial development with the resources available at that time. These factors permitted the inauguration of railway projects to the full extent of civil engineering technique as it then stood. This matching of civil and mechanical engineering led to the big railway schemes of the mid-1830s, in particular the Grand Junction, London & Birmingham, and Great Western railways. Without Rainhill and *Rocket* all such schemes would inevitably have been deferred.

*Rocket's* success was due almost entirely to the combination of the multitubular boiler with separate firebox and the blast-pipe exhaust, that is to the steam-generating equipment.[21] The boiler was suggested by Henry Booth, first treasurer and, in effect, first manager, of the LMR, and *Rocket* itself was entered by him and George Stephenson and its cost charged to the pair in the Forth Street books; but the whole of the design was the direct task of Robert Stephenson. This boiler was particularly suited to the stringent weight conditions imposed; nevertheless, without the blast pipe its evaporative powers would have been only frac-

tionally greater than established return-flue types.

Blast pipe and multitubular boiler with separate firebox were an individisible quantity which gave automatic regulation of the whole plant. Blast-pipe exhaust in single-flue and return-flue boilers could more easily tear the fire to bits, as it did at the Rainhill trials in *Sans Pareil*. Among the three actual competing engines *Rocket* and *Sans Pareil* had induced draught promoted by blast exhaust and *Novelty* had forced draught from mechanically-driven bellows.

In its mechanical arrangement *Rocket* was disappointing, particularly after the experience with *Lancashire Witch* and Robert's 1828 thoughts as to cylinder position; the angle of the cylinders was surprising, and the result was a bouncing movement on the springs. This was rectified in the Rocket-type locomotives ordered for the opening of the LMR, in which cylinder inclination was reduced to 8° from *Rocket's* 35°. But *Rocket* at 35° and on springs was superior in riding to the vertical-cylinder springless *Sans Pareil*, though perhaps inferior to *Novelty* which, though it had small vertical cylinders, had very good springs, and a bell-crank drive to long connecting rods which drove a double-throw crank axle — the first ever, though it was not in combination with inside cylinders. *Novelty* was also the first full tank engine, for it contained the small amount of fuel needed, and the water was in a tank below the platform.

In the contest each engine had to make 10 return trips over a 1¾-mile length of which an eighth of a mile at each end was allowed for acceleration and retardation, thus giving the equivalent of a 30-mile journey at speed and 35 miles total, with a trailing load three times the locomotive weight. After a stop for refuelling and rewatering the engine had straightway to make another 35 miles. This was the equivalent of a return journey between Liverpool and Manchester. The 4¼-ton *Rocket* hauled 13 tons and averaged 12.4mph for the 70 miles including the 38 end stops but not the 16min refuelling stop. The day after, when the 2¾-ton *Novelty* had broken down after one trip, *Rocket* gave the spectators a 'consolation display' when without any load at all it made two double trips at 30mph. On being tried again *Novelty* once more broke down, this time after about seven miles, and retired from the contest.

*Sans Pareil* completed 27½ miles of the 70 at an average approaching 15mph; then a defect in a feed pump lowered the water level and the fusible plug in the flue melted, so ending the test. Subsequently Hackworth and his family worked hard to create a belief that a cylinder cast by Stephenson had cracked and led to the bad results, but neither the judges nor other contemporary records made mention of that. Over the 27½ miles the coke consumption of

Sans Pareil was 1269lb or 46lb/mile contrasted with Rocket's 15½lb/mile; most of this went out the chimney as unburned fuel for Hackworth had contracted his blast pipe far too much by tapering, and the firing rate was the almost inconceivable figure, for a return-flue boiler, of 69lb/sfg/hr (pounds of coal per square foot of grate per hour), whereas that of Rocket, with a firebox that could more easily have taken a high firing rate, was only 30lb/sfg/hr.

Possibly Sans Pareil was the first engine to have a tapered blast pipe, for the evidence that Royal George had one previously is anything but sure; but it was not the first to have a contracted blast pipe. As that term was then understood it meant an area less than that of the exhaust port in the cylinder, and this was found in the double blast pipes of the SDR four-wheelers and in the twin up-turned final exhausts of Rocket, in which the end pipes were parallel. This was sufficient to make enough steam for Rocket to run its 70 miles, and had also been enough for the earlier Killingworth engines.

That the new era in public transport made possible by Rocket was appreciated at once by a few forward-thinking minds is shown by the words of Henry Booth early in 1830 before the formal opening of the LMR:[22] 'the sudden and marvellous change which has been effected in our ideas of time and space . . . it will pervade society at large . . . will influence more or less the whole tenor and business of life.'

First practical result of Rainhill was the immediate purchase of Rocket by the LMR and an order for four similar engines placed in October with Robert Stephenson & Co to be delivered in 1830 in time for opening day. Two more were ordered in February 1830, and another two later, These eight engines are listed in Table 1 which shows the stages of enlargement. All after Rocket had the lowered cylinders. From Phoenix all had a boiler 6in longer than before and a full-diameter smokebox in place of a swelled chimney base, and this had both a front tube-cleaning door and an ash-cleaning door below. These engines also had double slide valves in place of the single type in Nos 1 to 5.

Northumbrian and Majestic had the integral firebox; all the others had the Rocket type of separate firebox bolted to the boiler back with top and side steam and water connecting pipes. This completed the essentials of the locomotive boiler, which remained unchanged to the end. Second major development in Northumbrian was the provision of a vertical-plate frame taking driving axleboxes and cylinders, in place of the light flat bar frame used in Rocket.

The increase of some 50 per cent in tractive and boiler power over Rocket was enough for the ceremonies of the LMR official opening on 15 September 1830; but regular traffic and service quickly grew beyond the power and robustness even of Majestic, the last Rocket-type engine. However, swinging out in the Mersey estuary on board ship on opening day was the first of a new design that immediately superseded the Rocket type and provided much of the LMR motive power over the first five or six years.

This was Planet, in which Robert Stephenson's 1828 ideas of cylinder position came to fruition. It was an inside-cylinder outside-frame 2-2-0 as against the outside-cylinder inside-frame 0-2-2 Rocket type, but it had the same cylinder dimen-

Table 1  Rocket-type Locomotives, Liverpool & Manchester Railway, 1829-30[6]

| LMR No | Name | Delivery date | Wheel dia | Cylinder dimensions | No & dia of tubes and boiler length | Grate area | Evap. heating surface | Loco weight tons | Firebox | Smokebox |
|---|---|---|---|---|---|---|---|---|---|---|
| | | | ft in | in | in, and ft in | sq ft | sq ft | | | |
| 1 | Rocket[1] | 10/1829 | 4 - 8 | 8 x 17 | 25 @ 3.0; 6 - 0 | 6.0 | 138 | 4.3 | Separate | None |
| 2 | Meteor[2] | 1/1830 | 5 - 0 | 10 x 16 | 88 @ 2.0; 6 - 0 | 6.0 | 300 | 5.7 | Separate | None |
| 3 | Comet | 1/1830 | 5 - 0 | 10 x 16 | 90 @ 2.0; 6 - 0 | 6.0 | 308 | 5.7 | Separate | None |
| 4 | Arrow[4] | 2/1830 | 5 - 0 | 10 x 16 | 90 @ 2.0; 6 - 0 | 6.0 | 308 | 5.7 | Separate | None |
| 5 | Dart[5] | 2/1830 | 5 - 0 | 10 x 16 | 90 @ 2.0; 6 - 0 | 6.0 | 308 | 5.7 | Separate | None |
| 7 | Phoenix | 6/1830 | 5 - 0 | 11 x 16 | 90 @ 2.0; 6 - 0 | 6.1 | 310 | c6.5 | Separate | Separate |
| 9 | Northumbrian | 8/1830 | 5 - 0 | 11 x 16 | 132 @ 1.625; 6 - 6 | 6.1 | 412 | 7.35 | Integral | Separate |
| 8 | North Star[3] | 8/1830 | 5 - 0 | 11 x 16 | 90 @ 2.0; 6 - 0 | 6.1 | 310 | c6.5 | Separate | Separate |
| 11 | Majestic | 12/1830 | 5 - 0 | 11 x 16 | 130 @ 1.625; 6 - 6 | 6.4 | 407 | 7.35 | Integral | Separate |

[1] Sold to B. Thompson of Brampton 10/1836 for £300  
[2] Sold 3/1837 for £240  
[3] Sold to McKenzie (contractor) 12/1835 for £275  
[4] Sold in 1840 for £50  
[5] Broken up 4/1833  
[6] All built by Robt. Stephenson & Co; all with 50psi boiler pressure

sions and almost the same boiler size as *Northumbrian*. The horizontal cylinders were below the smokebox and were encased by prolongations of the smokebox side plates so that the gas could circulate round them and cut heat loss by radiation, a feature Robert Stephenson recorded was due to ideas he imbibed from Trevithick in South America. At first double slide valves were used, that is one complete short slide valve over each port and on a common spindle. Under date 30 September 1832 is a note in the Robert Stephenson & Co order book reading: 'Loco cylinders in future to work with single slides.' This was not acted on immediately, and LMR *Firefly* delivered March 1833 had double type.

Doubts about crank axle strength and safety led to four inner frames supplementing the main outside frames. All six were of wood baulks, but the outside pair were bound at the ends with iron straps and angles and had iron hornplates for all axleboxes. The inner frames ran only from rear cylinder covers to the throatplate and did not carry weight. Springs were below the outside boxes of the driving axle and above the leading carrying boxes.

*Planet's* wheels were of wood with iron tyres. The Stephensons may have felt the SDR plug type was not the thing for the higher speeds on the LMR, for 30mph was being peaked as early as 1830 in daily service. The wooden form became increasingly unsatisfactory, and though it lasted until about 1835, attempts were made from 1832 to get a good iron wheel.

Basically the Planet conception lasted until the end of steam, but many variations grew out of it, and the initial design itself had numerous detail modifications in the first two or three years. In one respect the early Planet type was superior to many locomotive concepts over the next 20 years in that its main wooden frame structure ran from end to end and not only supported the boiler-cylinder ensemble but took the drawgear at each end. Nevertheless for some reason by October 1832 trials were being made of intermediate drawgear attached to the firebox. In 1832 the four inside wooden frames gave place to iron frames attached to the firebox. This construction was applied also to the 0-4-0 Planets of 1831 known generally as the Samsons, built at first as bankers and then as freight power.

Inside fireboxes were mainly of iron in early Planets, and one engine, *Ajax*, was sent to Liverpool with a circulating pipe connecting the throatplate with the underside of the barrel adjacent to the smokebox. Boilers of 1831-33 Planets were by no means all the same, and some had considerably less heating surface than *Northumbrian*. Short wheelbase (5ft 3in to 5ft 8in) was a main defect of Planets, and gave a pitch and toss motion destruc-

tive both to rails and engine parts.

After a score of Planets the way was clear for the next step of a six-wheel engine, Robert Stephenson's 2-2-2 *Patentee* of 1833, a deliberate attempt to get a bigger machine with steadier riding and no increase in axle load. By the use of a bigger boiler it was expected that back pressure in the blast pipe could be reduced. The contracted blast pipe, which in 1829-30 had *made* the multitubular boiler, had by 1833 become a menace, for with engines limited to full cut-off the draught was so fierce with a taper top that copper boiler tubes and other parts had the briefest of lives. Main outside frames now became sandwich type, that is oak or ash baulks with $\frac{1}{4}$in iron flitching plates along each side.

Before this natural development from the Planets, Robert Stephenson & Co encountered its first serious rival as a locomotive builder: Edward Bury. In 1830 Bury had two locomotives on the LMR though they were still his own property. Of the first one, *Dreadnought*, little is known; the second, *Liverpool*, was an inside-cylinder crank-axle 0-4-0 with 6ft wheels, a size that raised the strong objections of George Stephenson as LMR engineer, as did the inside bar frames. The elder Stephenson's opposition prevented any proper trial of *Liverpool*, but after the engine was given a multitubular boiler and blast exhaust in place of the original convoluted tubes and bellows draught it worked for some years on the Bolton & Leigh.

Bury was not be be denied, and by 1832 had a 2-2-0 named *Liver* on the LMR and another on the Bolton & Leigh. He had proposed inside bar frames and inside cylinders, but Stephenson's actions resulted in him having to put on additional outside frames supporting axle bearings. However, he retained his inside bar frames. The firebox originally was circular in an endeavour to eliminate side stays, and it had a hemispherical top to the outside box, but again Stephenson insisted this be altered.

According to notes of John Dixon, the LMR resident engineer, *Liver* covered 25,600 miles in the first 12 or 13 months and was still in good working order; its coke consumption was as good as that of *Planet*. Trials between *Planet* and *Liver* when the latter was three months old showed respective coke consumptions of 0.51 and 0.49lb/ton-mile; and Anthony Harding, one of the LMR running employees, was severely reprimanded by the board for trying to influence results in favour of the Newcastle engine by loading its tender with picked coke. After 30,000 miles *Liver's* original iron inside firebox was reported in good order and not deteriorated. When *Liver* needed a new firebox in 1834 it was selected for the fitting of Chantor's special coal-burning firebox.

Though Bury had to stay his fireboxes he retained for many years the hemispherical top, and left to himself he did not use outside frames and axleboxes. While the locomotive was growing bigger and heavier through six-wheelers, and from 1837 by the opening of the broad-gauge GWR, he concentrated on four-wheelers and became the first apostle of the small-engine policy, having full scope for this when he was appointed locomotive superintendent of the London & Birmingham Railway (LBR) in 1838 while retaining his interest in the Clarence Street Foundry at Liverpool. His 2-2-0s and 0-4-0s had their major application on that railway, and by the mid-1840s sometimes as many as five could be seen at the head of principal passenger trains.

This mass application of Bury four-wheelers was due not to any technical superiority but to power politics, a Quaker section of the LBR board being rabidly anti-Stephenson and inspanning Bury as the most powerful rival. These men prevented any quote for locomotives being accepted from Robert Stephenson & Co while Robert himself was chief engineer of the railway, but they had Bury appointed to take charge of locomotive working on a contract basis and purchased as many of his locomotives as he advised were necessary.

*Patentee* in its way was as big a development over *Planet* as the latter was over *Rocket,* both in wheel arrangement and in basic construction. Trials with it began late in 1833, but at first the broad flangeless treads cut too deeply into the wooden switches used at that time. Also difficulty was found in getting sufficient adhesion weight; and not until these matters had been rectified, new cylinders

supplied, the inside frames strengthened, and more trials run did the LMR accept the engine in September 1834 at a price of £1000, which meant a loss to the Stephenson firm.

Six-wheel ideas originated at Newcastle in 1832, and the flangeless centre treads in each design were intended to improve crank-axle performance by taking away the end thrusts imposed from the flanges. At that time and for years after the crank axle was one of the weakest constituents, and from early 1832 the LMR was refusing crank axles of $4\frac{1}{8}$in dia as too weak. By the beginning of 1834 William Hutchinson at Forth Street had worked out standard journal and pin diameters for various wheel diameters and axle loads, and by the end of that year all axles were said to be 50 per cent stronger than in 1831, which meant $4\frac{3}{4}$in minimum dia of pin and journal. The coupled Planets *Samson* and *Goliah* of the LMR in 1831 had $5\frac{3}{8}$in dia crankpins and $5\frac{1}{2}$in dia inside bearings; the outer journals, however, were only $3\frac{1}{2}$in dia.

In 1833-4 several 0-4-2 and 2-2-2 Patentees were built for the LMR, Stanhope & Tyne (STR) and Leicester & Swannington (LSR) railways, and in 1834 the design was extended to an 0-6-0 named *Atlas* for the LSR which had a cylinder volume 40 per cent greater than that of any other English locomotive of the time, and 656sq ft of heating surface, 80 per cent more than that of *Patentee* itself. John Dixon did not think much of it, and when sent by the LMR to observe it he reported in January 1835 that it had '16in by 20in cyclinders, weighed 15 tons, was very slow in its movements, and did not appear to be much approved on that line.' The LMR

London & Birmingham 2-2-0 Bury bar-frame type of 1838 as running in the early 1860s after conversion to a tank locomotive.

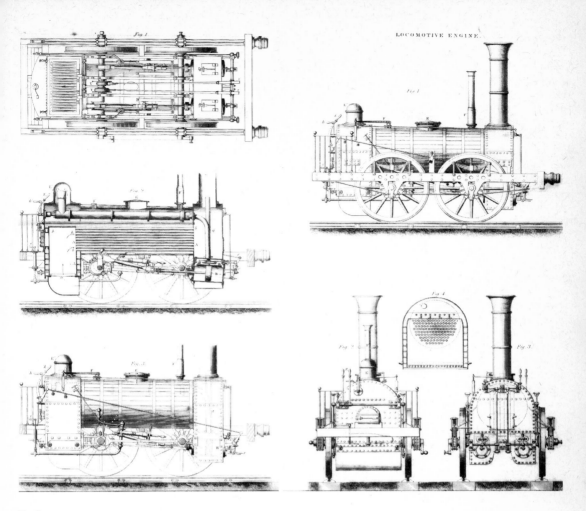

LOCOMOTIVE ENGINE.

Fig 3
Two four-coupled Planets *Samson* and *Goliah* were
built in 1831 for banking service on the Whiston and
Sutton inclines of the LMR, and the design was later
used for goods engines. 5ft wheels; double slide valves
with actuation from spindles and cross levers in front

therefore decided on 0-4-2s rather than copy *Atlas*.

With the 2-2-2 type and 5ft or 5ft 6in wheels the
Planet arrangement of horizontal cylinders could be
retained; but the 0-4-2 and 0-6-0 layouts
necessitated up-sloping cylinders in which the piston
rod lay below the leading axle; the slide valves were
above the cylinders and the valve rods above the
axle. In some early examples the smokebox sides
were still extended down round the cylinder barrels
to conserve heat.

Despite a few early lines like STR and LSR, the
LMR was still the proving ground for locomotives
and until 1838 much of the development and testing
work was done there. On it vertical-cylinder types
like the Roberts *Experiment* and Galloway's
*Manchester* received their *quietus*, and others like
the Forrester outside-cylinder outside-frame models

first showed their performance. Two further brief
experiments on the LMR were the fitting of *Rocket*
with Lord Dundonald's rotary engine (*not* a turbine
type) in October 1834 (it did not turn a wheel while
so fitted); and, secondly, two or three engines were
fitted late in 1832 with Perkins circulator tubes in
the firebox, but only *Vesta* seems to have done any
work while so fitted, and ran 6510 miles between 24
October 1832 and 4 January 1833. As satisfactory
payment terms with Perkins could not be arranged
these tubes were removed.

To a much greater extent than the SDR the LMR
took, or had thrust upon it, the birth pains of the
locomotive and those of an economic public railway
system at one and the same time, and this led to
alternating emphasis on one or the other. First,
Rocket-type locomotives had to be replaced by
Planets. Long before design troubles of the latter
had been solved, traffic requirements called for six-
wheelers which brought fresh design and construction problems to which no real solutions were
forthcoming in the 1830s, and even for LMR con-

25

ditions were scarcely finalised by Dewrance's Bird class 2-2-2s in the early 1840s, one of which, *Ostrich*, was the first engine to have Babbit metal (or whitemetal) bearings.

Concurrent with intensified traffic and speed demands, and difficulties of locomotive construction, came a gradual increase in coke consumption that took the attention of the board. Rocket-type engines used 25 to 30lb/mile of coke with four light coaches, and Planets in 1831-33 around 20 to 30lb with heavier loads. De Pambour[23] recorded that in 1834 consumption with eight-coach passenger trains at 24mph average was 26 to 35lb/mile, and that 120-ton goods trains at 17mph used 38 to over 40lb/mile, all these being running consumptions. By 1838-9 with larger engines and higher speeds the consumption with seven-coach passenger trains was 48-49lb/mile, and with goods trains around 100 tons weight the average had risen to 54lb/mile.

To counter these increases ashpans with front dampers were introduced in the mid-1830s, but additional back dampers did not come until the 1840s. The board tightened up driving and operating regulations, and supplied coke in weighed bags to the tenders; it was reckoned the equivalent of 7lb/mile was saved if the safety valves never blew off. But the most far-reaching development in the coke-saving drive was the initiation of slide-valve experiments in 1838-39, described in Chapter 6.

The results of these endeavours were not available when the Grand Junction (GJR) and LBR were opened in 1837 and 1838, the former with Patentee types by four different makers and the latter with Bury 2-2-0s to which were soon added 0-4-0s for goods trains. The GJR lot were poor and maintained the service only with much trouble; a report at the first annual meeting after opening was that every one of the crank axles in the first 25 locomotives had broken or had been replaced. Nevertheless at that time GJR locomotives made the longest through runs in the country, 90 miles between Birmingham and Liverpool. They commonly made a return trip in the day but were not diagrammed the following day.

Main reasons for the poor construction and performance of locomotives through the 1830s were first the whole industrial environment and, secondly, the inability to understand and see into operation the ideas of the forward thinkers or ensure adequate manufacture. Nor were the materials available up to the new duties put upon them particularly in the three new power transport avenues: ships, rail and road, where 'movement' was added to the function of a power plant, a principle well understood by George Stephenson, who always used the term 'loco-motive'.

A common emotion in steam locomotive circles for years past has been admiration for the fine craftsmen of old, but through the 1830s there were few such men and comparatively few developed in the succeeding decade. Employees in the earliest locomotive works were no different from those flocking to all the other developing manufactures; they came partly from agriculture, but more extensively from the almost homeless and uneducated population that had been growing in England and Scotland for about two centuries, and they found in the locomotive trade and on railways just what they found in the mines and the Lancashire and Yorkshire mills: that, to quote Lewis Mumford,[24] the two leading requirements of the factory system were castration of skill and discipline of starvation.

For many years private builders and railways hired and sacked men, including drivers and firemen, or altered their wage rates, at a moment's notice according to immediate trade conditions. The constant drift engendered by these methods was accentuated by the fact that by 1840 well over 30 different works in England alone had made one or more locomotives. Yet by that time scarcely three of them could deliver a locomotive that could take up its job straightaway and get on with it without interminable adjustments and alterations. Nor were maintenance and operation any better handled, and railways were in constant trouble with their motive power and working conditions.

Typical are notes in the Stephenson description book No 1 relating to *Firefly* despatched to the LMR from Newcastle on 18 March 1833: 'This engine wanted some stays near the bottom tubes which had to be put in at Liverpool or Manchester, and it was likewise found with seams [cracks] in the plates of the inside firebox. When she had run 3000 miles she began to burst tubes and by 15 May when she had run 4900 miles she had burst 8 or 10 copper tubes, the brass ones all stand. She broke her crank axle after running 28,500 miles.' Of LMR *Pluto* the same book records: 'Began running 17 October 1832. First tube burst December 20 after running 7170 miles. The tube when put in weighed $11\frac{1}{4}$lb and when taken out $6\frac{1}{2}$lb, having lost $4\frac{3}{4}$lb.' The LMR worked its new locomotive hard, for *Pluto* must have made two double trips a day.

# 5 Five Great Types

Through the decade 1833-42 appeared the five main systems of construction that covered the great majority of British locomotives for the remainder of the century. These types were based on frame location and construction and the position of the cylinders as shown in Table 2. Apart from a few locomotives on the Great Western, only two of the five remained in

Fig 4
Section and plan of Stephenson Patentee 2-2-2 of 1837-8 with 5ft flangeless driving wheels. No ashpan; damper centre-hinged on blast pipe in chimney and operated by rod from footplate. Double eccentric gab motion with up-turned gabs; form of eccentric shown was in use only a few years

new construction after the 1880s, a contraction due as much as anything to the availability of large rolled iron plates from around 1860 and of steel plates from 1875.

The Patentee type began in 1833 with inside cylinders, outside sandwich main frames running from end to end and carrying all axleboxes, and four subsidiary inside iron plate frames running only between the cylinders and the firebox throat plate. The inside frames had non-sprung bearings round the crank axle, supporting that member to some degree but mainly taking the piston thrust, and adopted because of the weakness and unreliability of double-throw cranks. Soon the two innermost

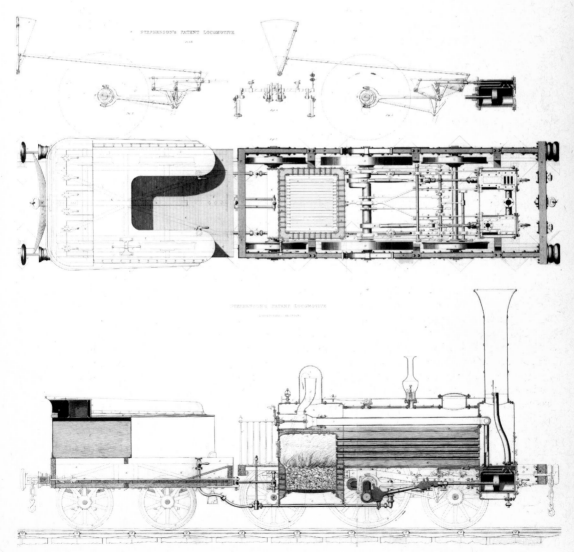

27

frames were brought together forward of the crank axle and housed one bearing, making five in all instead of six. Later still the number of inside frames was reduced to two, and after about 1850 they ran from end to end, and many came to carry sprung axleboxes. Thus the design developed into the double-frame type, at first with sandwich outside frames and then with plate outside frames. This last development continued in new construction into the Grouping (1923) era on the GWR. For the first few years of Patentee construction the cylinders were supported only by the smokebox side plates and by the back-end angle attachment to the inside frames, and so they were weakly held and were subject to slight movement that reacted on the crank axle among other parts.

By 1838-40 this design had become the standard of all builders except Bury, for Robert Stephenson's claims in his patent No 6484 of 7 October 1833 were only for details such as steam brakes, flangeless driving wheel treads and tubular wheel spokes, and no other type was adaptable immediately to the primitive manufacturing resources and lack of designing experience.

Around 1837 Sharp Roberts introduced a modification to the outside frames that distinguished

'Sharpies' from other makes: the top of the frame was curved down on each side of the driving axle so that the horn plates for the end carrying axles did not have to be so deep. Generally the long separate horn plates were flimsy and whipped laterally, so loosening the bolts and necessitating much maintenance work. In the Sharp engines the horn plates were soon forged on to the main flitch plates of the sandwich frame instead of being separated pieces bolted or rivetted on. In the Stephenson-type Patentees small-diameter bolted tie-rods connected the horn plate bottoms along each side, but these were unnecessary in the Sharpies. The curved frame top was advantageous with the then general driving wheel diameter of 5ft and 5ft 6in and became essential when 6ft wheels were adopted. Further Sharp Roberts features were trailing wheels of the same diameter as the leading pair, and a large dome immediately behind the chimney to get a shorter dry pipe and increase the steam space in the boiler. About 500 Sharpie 2-2-2s were built from 1837 to the end of 1849.

Daniel Gooch in 1839-40 also began to forge the horn plates in one with the flitching plates. He also adopted a slotted form of flitching plate that increased the longitudinal and lateral strength around the horns, though at first he retained the Stephenson horizontal frame-top line with a long single baulk of timber. This slotted shape lasted in new construction on the GWR until 1889, and the last survivor was withdrawn in the 1930s.

Broad-gauge *North Star* of 1837, the first really successful Patentee; slightly rebuilt and renewed, as it was up to scrapping in 1907.

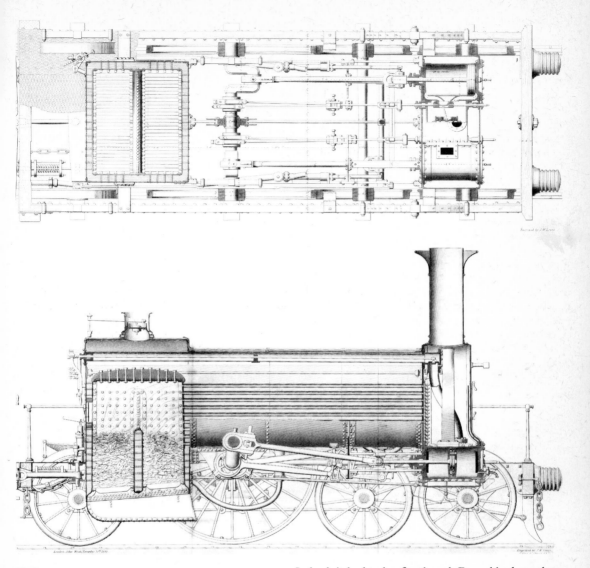

Fig 5
Broad-gauge standard express engine for over 40
years, the Iron Duke class, with outside sandwich
frames, inside subsidiary plate frames, and very stiff
tie-in of boiler and frame structure

The sandwich frame began with a 3in ash plank
and $\frac{1}{4}$in iron flitching plates; but as the size of
engines grew the wood thickness increased to 4in
and plate thickness to $\frac{1}{2}$in. Then oak was substituted
for ash, and later again the baulk gave place to oak
or teak packing pieces and iron spacers distributed
throughout the frame. These forms were used on the
broad gauge until the end in 1892, for they were
said to help an easier ride on the non-elastic
longitudinal timbers that gave continuous support
to the rail foot.

Earliest really successful Patentee was Stephenson's *North Star* for the 7ft gauge GWR in 1838.

Indeed, it had to be, for though Brunel had not then
received any of the miscellaneous collection of
locomotives he first ordered, he wrote to Robert
Stephenson on 4 July 1837: 'I expect you will furnish us with an engine of the best construction . . .
and I look forward to having such an engine as
never was before.' He got it, though *North Star* was
already built and simply had to be converted in rail
gauge from 6ft to 7ft. In 1838 Gooch adopted its
principles, and the first 11 of his own engines formed the first GWR Star class. Of the first three of
these Brunel wrote in 1839: 'Another Star would
make us comparatively easy, particularly the directors, who consider the Stars double Stars I suppose,
as they always reckon them as two.' This design was
enlarged into the 29-ton *Great Western* in 1846.
After breaking the leading axle that engine was
rebuilt to 4-2-2, and the resulting design was further

enlarged into the Iron Duke class, of which 29 were built from 1847 to 1859, and remained the broad-gauge standard express passenger engine until the abolition in 1892.

Strictly the Dukes and following Lord of the Isles batch were 2-2-2-2s for the two leading axles were separate in the main sandwich frame, though they shared the same spring on each side. The two subsidiary inside iron plate frames reached only from cylinders to throat plate, but sprung axleboxes were located in both inside and outside frames, and a large iron bracket rivetted to the bottom of the boiler barrel carried a fifth (centre) bearing for the driving axle. This was unsprung, and circular tie-rods and pin joints connected the bracket to the throat plate at the rear and to the cylinder cross stay at the front.

The outside frames were tied together directly only by the light footplate structure and by the back and front wooden buffer beams, but two sloping stanchions on each side gave a bolted connection of the boiler-firebox ensemble to the sandwich frame. This was another detail found in the early Patentees of 1833-35; it was eliminated from many built during the 1840s and 1850s, but was retained in some new construction until the mid-1860s, as in the

Sturrock's express 4-2-2 on the GNR, 1853. Intended for through runs above 100 miles and 60 mph top speed.

NER 0-6-0s of the 524 class.

*Iron Duke*'s boiler was also tied to the two inside iron frames by a large rivetted under-belly stay, so that in total effect the boiler was just as much part of the whole frame structure as were the sandwich sides. Moreover the intermediate drawbar was still connected to the firebox backplate, but these broad-gauge locomotives had spring intermediate buffers, a fitting not then found on standard-gauge engines.

This complete integration of boiler, frame and drawgear was a characteristic of all Patentee-type locomotives,[25] as well as of other types, up to 1848-50, when gradually the inside frames were made full length, expansion brackets were introduced, and the intermediate drawbar connection was made to the dragbox. Despite these defects the iron boiler shells of many of the Iron Duke and Lord of the Isles classes ran over 600,000 miles.

Patentee forms on standard gauge were found in new construction to around 1870, and in modified form for another 15 years. They included such well-known examples as the so-called Large Hawthorn 2-2-2s on the GNR (1852-53), *Plews* of the York, Newcastle & Berwick and *Queen* of the NBR (1846), Sturrock's 7ft 6in 4-2-2 No 215 of the GNR (1853), the GWR standard-gauge Gooch 2-2-2s of 1855 – the first locomotives built by Beyer Peacock, a long line of Kirtley 2-2-2s, 2-4-0s and 0-6-0s on the Midland, and Cudworth's 7ft Mail

Crewe-type 2-4-0T, one of over 100 conversions from 2-4-0 tender engines from 1859 to 1870.

engines on the South Eastern. In *Plews* and other Hawthorn Patentees the cylinders were secured to both sandwich outside and plate inside frames, and their centres lay just inside the wheels, thus producing what was almost a half-crank engine. The eccentrics lay between the wheel and the outside axle box; the boxes in the inside frame were sprung, and this frame ran forward from the throat plate to the front buffer beam.

Sandwich- or double-frame 0-6-0s were built until the mid-1880s and included the Sturrock steam-tender machines on the GNR (1864-66) and the Fletchers on the NER (to 1882). Though stemming in direct line from the LSR *Atlas* of 1834, many of those built from around 1870 had rolled-plate outside frames without sandwich and were more correctly double-frame engines, for the inner frames were retained and the crank axle continued to have four bearings though the coupled axles had only two. As late as 1908 the East & West Junction Railway had two new 0-6-0s with double frames, and the GWR revived the type as late as 1936 in 10 superheater Earl-class 4-4-0s with axle loads under 16 tons for the ex-Cambrian lines.

Poor performance of the first 40 Patentees on the GJR from its opening in 1837 led directly to the evolution of a second great class, the so-called Crewe type, linked erroneously for a century and more with the name of Alexander Allan, chief foreman at Crewe shops from 1843 to 1853.[26]

Spurred on by the chief engineer Joseph Locke, the GJR locomotive superintendent of 1840-1, W. B. Buddicom, first eliminated the four thin inside plate frames and bearings of the Patentees and replaced them with two thicker frames just inside the wheels. He recorded in 1840 the difficulty in procuring sound and reliable crank axles, and after trying a couple of Forrester outside-cylinder outside-frame 2-2-2s he evolved an outside-cylinder 2-2-2 in which the cylinders lay between inside and outside plate frames, both full length. The crank axle had bearings only in the two inside frames, and the carrying axles had bearings only in the outside frames. This brought the cylinders closer together and eliminated the flycrank drive of the Forresters, whose outside frames and cylinders still further outside brought a motion that led to them being known colloquially as 'the boxers'. Just as important as all this, Buddicom's design eliminated the frame-throatplate fixed connection, and the connection of the intermediate drawbar to the firebox which was such a defect in other types.

From 1843 to 1857 Crewe works built practically nothing other than standard 2-2-2s and 2-4-0s of this type, and with no striking increase in power, for cylinders went up only from 13in by 20in to 16in by 20in, boiler pressure from 75 to 100psi, and weight from $17\frac{1}{2}$ to 21 tons. Even *Cornwall*, with 8ft 6in drivers, scaled only about 26 tons when rebuilt to Crewe type from its original design with malformed boiler slung below the driving axle.

'Crewe' principles were developed far above Crewe dimensions in 2-2-2 and 2-4-0 wheel

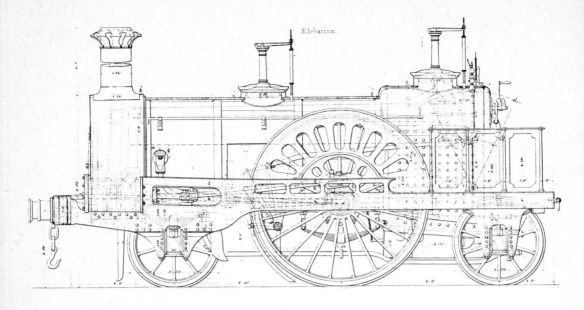

Elevation.

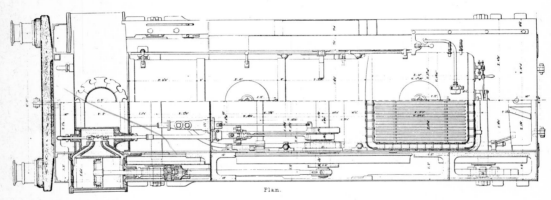

Plan.

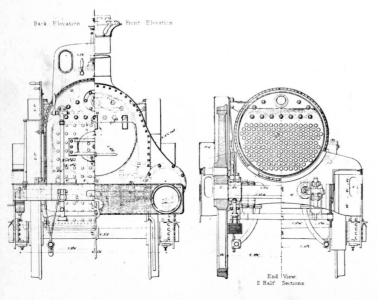

Back Elevation.    Front Elevation.

End View.
2 Half Sections.

Fig 6
Apogee of the Crewe-built
Crewe-type, Trevithick's 7ft
2-2-2s of 1852-7. The 1857
batch were the first engines to
have the castellated chimney top
usually associated with the name
of Ramsbottom. Note old Crewe
standard regulator with handle
on spiral quadrant; also grate
with slope down to rear

arrangements on the Caledonian and Great Eastern railways (1859-63), and later with 4-4-0s on the Highland Railway. Locke and Buddicom also sponsored the type on early French railways, and in the late 1850s and early 1860s the Canada works at Birkenhead built 4-4-0s for the Great Western of Canada and for the Finnish State Railways.

While the Stephenson Patentees, early Sharpies, and other builds were noising their way along the indifferent tracks of the few main and secondary railways opened during the 1830s, a new arrangement was announced in the patent of John Gray,[27] for inside-cylinder locomotives with an outside through plate frame for the leading and trailing carrying axles of a 2-2-2 and an inside plate frame to take the boxes of the crank axle. This was intended to give steady riding and stability while retaining simplicity, a train of thought that may have led Gray to his lack of fear of a high centre of gravity. At the time of the patent Gray was a mechanical assistant on the LMR, but from 1839 to 1844 he was locomotive superintendent of the Hull & Selby and in 1845-6 of the LBSCR.

First engines of this form were built to Gray's design by Shepherd & Todd, of Leeds, in 1840 for the Hull & Selby. In after years the type was known more often as the Jenny Lind because, under the influence of Gray, David Joy as leading draughtsman of E. B. Wilson & Co drew out a 2-2-2 in 1846-7

Fig 7
Section through the first Wilson Jenny Lind of 1847. Drawing believed to be a litho of David Joy's original coloured drawing. Inside frames and intermediate drawgear tied to firebox

that Wilson adopted as a standard and built an appreciable number for many railways. The first one of all, LBSCR No 70, was named *Jenny Lind* after the elegant Swedish soprano, then in her prime in England. Other builders followed suit in the 1850s. As far as is known, Gray never received a penny from this part of his patent, and he may have felt it was scarcely valid.

James Fenton, the Wilson manager, had the pressure of these Jennies raised to 120lb from Gray's 100lb. Gray himself was a pioneer of higher pressures, using 90lb in 1839-40 when other engineers were content with 70-75lb, but his valve gear was intended to get some use out of it. According to Joy[28] this higher pressure was one of the main reasons for success; the other was the inclusion of Stephenson link motion. Mechanically the early Wilson Jennies were flimsy. Gray's warnings from 1841 of the need for stiff frames, particularly round the horns, were neglected. Neither frame gave any support to the other; the cylinders were poorly held; the back drawbar pull was to a bracket on the firebox; Gray's excellent feature of a high centre of gravity was not perpetuated and the boiler pitch was $6\frac{1}{2}$in lower than that of the concurrent Hackworth-built Grays; the whole arrangement and attachments showed the 23-year old Joy's inexperience.

Fortunately the design was capable of immediate strengthening. From the mid-1850s the inner frames were carried from end to end, the outer frames were deepened and thickened, and the firebox connection of the drawbar was given up. Thus it was engines built 1855-61 to the revised scantlings that lasted

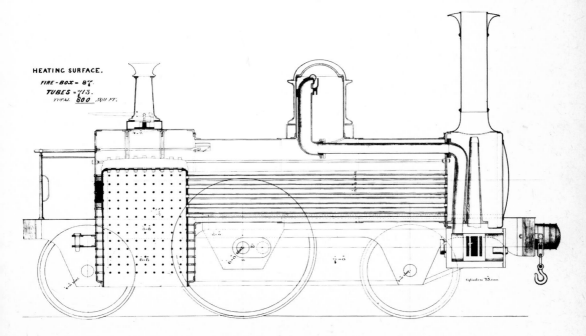

HEATING SURFACE.
FIRE-BOX = 87.
TUBES = 713.
TOTAL 800 SQR FT.

Jenny-Sharp 2-2-2T of 1849 built for the opening of the Manchester, South Junction & Altrincham. (N. W. Museum of Science)

longest; with the usual thorough rebuildings and reboilerings some of them, such as the Beyer Peacock 2-2-2s for the Edinburgh & Glasgow, ran in service to the end of World War I.

From 1847 Edward Wilson himself did high-pressure sales drives that kept the Railway Foundry books in good state for some years, with Jennies for a dozen railways. So successful was he that Sharp Bros had to enlarge and revise the Patentee-origin Sharpies into a 'Jenny Sharp' to keep their order book going, and this revision was done under Charles Beyer. In essence four sizes were built by Wilson between 1847 and 1857. They were: (a) the Jennies (15in by 20in cylinders); (b) enlarged Jennies (16in by 20in); (c) big Jennies (16in by 22in); and (d) the 1853 model (15in by 22in and 16in by 20in). Some of the big Jennies had midfeather fireboxes with 130 to 150sq ft of surface, and a total evaporative surface up to 1300sq ft contrasted with 800sq ft of the 1847 Jennies.

Unlike the Patentee sandwich-frame design, Gray's type could not cover fully the 0-6-0, though he himself had some six-coupled engines built for the Hull & Selby in which the leading axle had outside frame and boxes with a flycrank for the leading coupling rod pin. In 2-2-2, 2-4-0 and 0-4-2 layouts, Gray's ideas or modifications of them were built as late as the 1890s. Stirling's 7ft 6in singles on the GNR (1886-93) were the most impressive of the single-driver pattern, reaching 41 tons weight and a 17.5-ton axle load. Almost every large railway in England and Scotland except the Caledonian had

Gray-Jenny single-drivers, and the first two locomotives constructed at the Wolverhampton works of the GWR were of that type.

Fourth of the main categories to be developed slightly preceded the Crewe type but did not have a steady development. This was the outside-cylinder inside-frame type, the precursor of which was by Stirling of Dundee in 1839-40 for the Arbroath & Forfar line. In these engines the cylinders were steeply inclined and were attached to the smokebox and to a large slidebar casting bolted to the frames. The plate frames were shallow and had horn plates bolted on like a Patentee. In 1840 similar engines but with horizontal cylinders attached to the frames were built on Clydeside for one of the lines to Ayrshire. In both builds the intermediate drawbar was free of the firebox, but that box was attached to the frames. This principle, but with the back end of the boiler free of the frames and of the drawgear, and expansion brackets introduced, eventually developed into the type that lasted longest, and was maintained up to the end of new construction in 1960. By chance, both first and last examples had steeply inclined cylinders, the Dundee engines at 1 in 4½ and the BR class 9 2-10-0s at 1 in 10.

Despite its advantages, and the inherent weakness

Fig 8
Early example of outside-cylinder and inside-frame construction was to two 2-2-2Ts ordered from Sharp Bros in 1846 by the Manchester & Birmingham, which had become the NE Division of the LNWR when the engines were delivered in 1847. In their first 18 months these engines covered about 50,000 miles apiece on the Macclesfield branch on a coke consumption averaging 25lb/mile

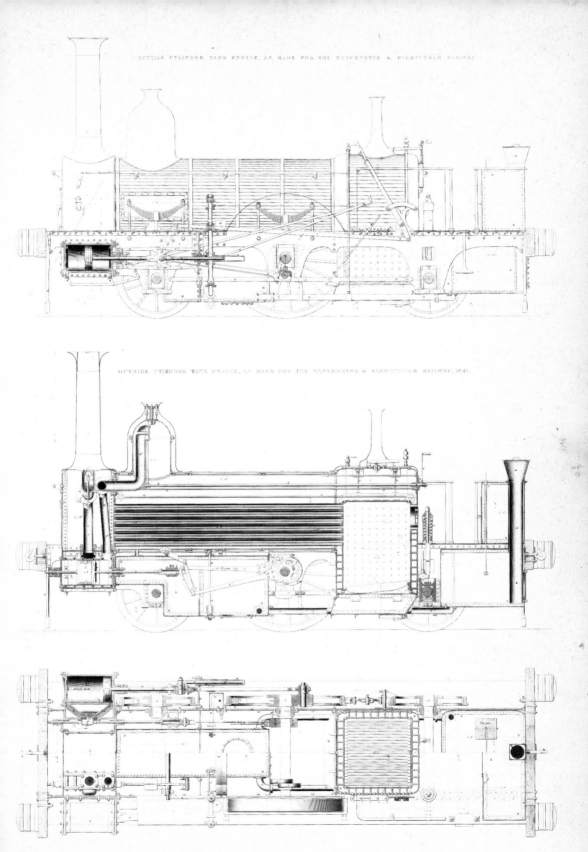

OUTSIDE CYLINDER TANK ENGINE, AS MADE FOR THE MANCHESTER & BIRMINGHAM RAILWAY.

OUTSIDE CYLINDER TANK ENGINE, AS MADE FOR THE MANCHESTER & BIRMINGHAM RAILWAY, 1847.

35

of crank axles, the outside-cylinder inside-frame layout with cylinders horizontal or nearly so was applied sparsely for many years. After a few Stephenson long-boiler engines (referred to later), desultory 2-2-2s on the Lancashire & Yorkshire (LYR) in 1849, 2-2-2s and 2-4-0s on the London & South Western (LSWR) in 1855-9, and 0-6-0s, 0-4-2s and 2-2-2s on the Glasgow & South Western (GSWR) and other Scottish lines were the main groups until John Ramsbottom built his 60 Problem 2-2-2s for the LNWR at Crewe in 1859-61. The most striking feature of those locomotives, sometimes known as the 'wobblers' from the motion arising from short wheelbase and widely spaced cylinders, was not the 7ft 6in driving wheels nor the first English use of injectors but the fact that the boiler, smokebox, slide valves and other details were standard with the inside-cylinder 5ft wheel 0-6-0s of the DX class. The Problems also were the first to be given tender water scoops, following Ramsbottom's invention of 1860.

Even this comparatively large group did not set a fashion. On the LNWR they were the last two-cylinder outside-cylinder locomotives built until the disappearance of the company in the 1923

Grouping; and they were the last main-line 2-2-2s with outside cylinders and single inside frames to be built for home lines.

Over the two decades from 1859 interesting applications of outside cylinders and inside frames included the first two English 4-4-0s on the SDR (1860); J. Beattie's 2-4-0T class on the LSWR from 1863; Sinclair's 2-4-0 on the Eastern Counties (1859-60) and 2-4-2T on the GER (1864); the well-known Metropolitan 4-4-0T from 1864; and three unsuccessful batches of 4-4-0s, viz W. G. Beattie's 20 engines for the LSWR (1876-7); the Adams engines on the GER (1876), and the Conner-Brittain class on the Caledonian (1876). Only after the Adams 4-4-0 classes on the LSWR from 1879 onwards, and the smaller version on the Eastern & Midlands, did the outside-cylinder inside-frame principle become more widely accepted for tender engines, and it was really extended only when large Atlantics and 4-6-0s were introduced at the end of the century.

Examples of the fifth major group, inside cylinders and inside end to end plate frames, began with Stephenson's patent long-boiler engines in 1841. The sketchy frames of the first construction were developed by the mid-1840s into deep slotted sections that took the axlebox guides without bolted, rivetted or forged horn plates, the main plates themselves coming well below axle centre line. This, applicable also to outside-cylinder engines, was one of the greatest single improvements made in British

Fig 9
Celebrated as efficient performers on very light trains were Ramsbottom's 60 Problem-class 2-2-2s built at Crewe 1859-61. Outside cylinders and inside frames. First line-service locomotives to have injectors

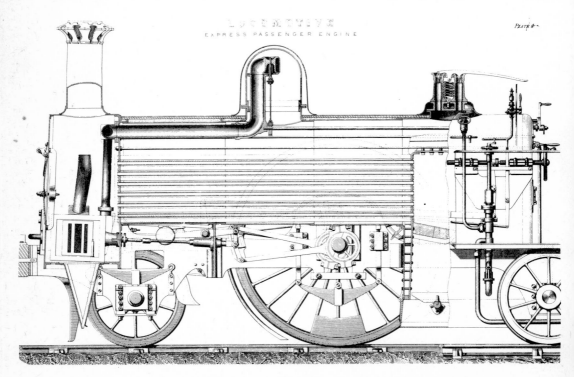

The first really standard engine to be built in large
numbers (943 from 1858 to 1875) — the Ramsbottom
DX 0-6-0 as built in the late 1860s. (British Railways)

McConnell's Bloomer 2-2-2 of 1851-2 with inside
cylinders and inside through plate frames.

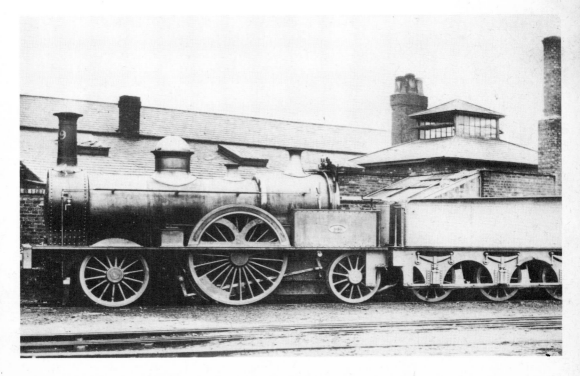

locomotive frame structures. From 1846 Sharp Bros began to forge-weld the axlebox guides as part of the frame. This method has been credited to Charles Beyer as chief engineer of the firm, and that may well be so; certainly in later years Beyer Peacock built many engines in which the whole frame was thickened outside and inside round the horns, so that axle bearings were centred in the frame.

Despite construction through the 1840s the in-side-cylinder inside through-frame design, as built thence well on into the Grouping era, really arrived with McConnell's first Bloomer-class 2-2-2s on the LNWR (Southern Division) in 1851. Additional to the frame and cylinder location, and resulting clean appearance with all axleboxes between the wheels and no outside rods, these locomotives were noteworthy in having 150lb boiler pressure at a time when LNWR Northern Division engines did not exceed 90lb and other railways were using 110-120lb. As with Sturrock's almost coincident introduction of 150lb on the GNR, pressure was soon reduced to 120lb. The Bloomers also had a high centre of gravity for the boiler pitch was 7ft 1in at a time when Crampton engines were still running with boilers pitched at 4ft 6in to 4ft 9in. In this McConnell was following John Gray, who from 1840 pitched his boilers well up and told the Gauge Commissioners in 1845 he was not worried by a high centre of gravity.

McConnell applied these same principles of frame location and high boiler pitch to big 0-6-0s (the Wolverton Goods) over the years 1854-62, and may be called the originator of the classic English 0-6-0 with inside cylinders, inside through frames, and firebox dropped between second and third axles. The advantages of this layout were not widely appreciated, and no other principal class for a home railway was built until Crewe began to turn out in 1858 the DX class, which eventually numbered 943 on the LNWR and LYR. Throughout the 1860s few railways adopted the inside frame for goods engines except for a few long-boiler engines on the SDR.

Most powerful for many years were the six 40-ton Stirling 0-6-0s built at Doncaster 1871-4 with cylinders no less than 19in by 28in and boiler pressure of 140lb. The large cylinder size, even in conjunction with a boiler pitch of 7ft, led to the slide valves being positioned beneath the cylinders, but they were horizontal, and a rocking-shaft drive was needed from the die-block. Stroudley, in his 38-ton LBSCR 0-6-0 of 1873, inclined the $17\frac{1}{4}$in by 26in cylinders downwards and the underneath slide valves upwards, a practice he followed in the later express 0-4-2 Gladstone class.

Numerous variations of these five main constructional principles were found over the years. None had a lasting influence on practice, but Robert

South Devon broad-gauge 4-4-0T *Zebra* of 1866 with inside plate frames.

Stephenson's long-boiler type may be mentioned here, for it was built in two of the constructions listed.[30] The long-boiler patent[31] contained at least one further important provision that did become a widely adopted feature for another 80 years, whereas long-boiler engines except for relatively few mineral types were not built after 1850.

Stephenson's object in placing all axles in front of the firebox was to get a longer barrel and more tube heating surface in six-wheel locomotives without increasing the wheelbase over the then existing small turntable size. He emphasised also that in the normal type with the rear axle behind the firebox the fireboxes had been increasing in size though barrel length had remained the same; thus smokebox gas temperatures had increased and more heat was lost. Ample firebox heating surface and volume were not so necessary for the coke fuel then used. Boiler ratios as understood in the 20th century were unthought of, and the relation of blast pipe to boiler proportions was not evaluated. In 1849 Ramsbottom inveighed that since 1842 heating surfaces had gone up $2\frac{1}{2}$ times but that blast pipe nozzle area had not increased at all, and he inferred that part of the stronger blast (and increased back pressure) was due to the long-boiler principle.

For slow-speed mineral services with much lie-by time the short wheelbase, comparatively small grate, and the ample water capacity in the barrel made the long-boiler 0-6-0 effective and economic, and such engines ran usually only at speeds where the unsteady motion was not inordinate, for the main disadvantage of the type, whatever the wheel arrangement, was the short wheelbase and heavy overhang at the back end that gave rough riding. Stephenson was undeterred by this and referred to the numerous Bury 2-2-0s and 0-4-0s with overhung hemispherical fireboxes, but he conveniently forgot the controversy and government investigation into the merits and demerits of four-wheelers and six-wheelers in 1840-1 that followed the fatal derailment of a Braithwaite-built Bury-type on the Eastern Counties. These particular engines had 6ft wheels, larger than any Bury make after *Liverpool* in 1830. A study at this time showed 630 locomotives on British and foreign railways excluding North America, of which two-thirds were six-wheelers, 159 of them Patentee type built at Stephenson's works. Stephenson is said to have adopted the outside cylinders for long-boiler engines from 1844 with export and licence orders in view, for crank axle manufacture in Europe was still unreliable.

To ameliorate the defects of the outside-cylinder long-boiler engine with cylinders ahead of the leading wheels, and firebox behind the trailers, a redesign brought the cylinders behind the leading wheels. This new location was applied to a few 2-4-0s, but it brought new wheel arrangements of 2-2-2-0 and 2-2-2-2. Among these was the so-called *Great A* 2-2-2-0 of the York & North Midland that figured prominently in the Gauge Commission trials of 1846, not because it was the last word in standard-gauge power but because it was the newest.

To get adequate steam space above the small firebox many of the early long-boiler engines had gothic fireboxes rising well above the barrel, another practice of Bury origin for it followed the concepts of that builder's hemispherical top dating from 1830, and of the haycock box. Only a few of the gothic boxes lasted beyond the first reboilerings,

but one or two in 0-6-0s were still in service 1870-5.

Until the coming of McConnell's normal 0-6-0 in 1854 all the most powerful goods engines in the country were long-boiler 0-6-0s, particularly those 28-ton 18in by 24in types under McConnell's own charge on the Southern Division of the LNWR. From 1845 the MSL also had 24-ton 0-6-0s of this type and size, and the cylinder capacity was not exceeded in 0-6-0s in the 50 further years of life of the MSL. Over the first 40,000 miles of life one of these 1845 engines cost £1050 for fuel, repairs, spares and crew wages, and on trial hauled a 600-ton freight train from Manchester to Crewe at 13.7mph average, but at the enormous firing rate of 140lb/sfg/hr. Long-boiler 0-6-0s were built down to 1875 for the SDR section of the NER, and the last one, No 1275, now at York Museum, was not withdrawn until 1920.

The five main forms of frame and cylinder layout as listed in Table 2 were applied for many years almost entirely to four-wheel and six-wheel locomotives (2-2-0, 0-4-0, 2-2-2, 2-4-0, 0-4-2, 0-6-0), but from the 1870s rolled plates of any needed length and the evolution of much better shop equipment and methods meant the growing demands for power and speed involving eight-wheel engines could be met best with through inside frames, with either inside or outside cylinders, and in turn this resulted in greater production of 4-4-0s and 4-2-2s in both forms, and the gradual disappearance of the other principles from new construction.

Table 2  Main Types of British Locomotive Construction[1]

| No | Description | Cylinder position | Main frame location | Main frame construction | Subsidiary frame and location | Dates |
|----|-------------|-------------------|---------------------|-------------------------|-------------------------------|-------|
| 1 | Patentee | Inside | Outside | Sandwich; wood with iron flitching plates both sides | Inside; plate; 2 to 5 in number | 1833-70 |
| 2 | Crewe | Outside | Inside | End-to-end plate | Outside; end-to-end plate taking carrying boxes | 1841-92 |
| 3 | Gray-Jenny Lind | Inside | Inside | Plate; taking driving boxes | Outside; plate taking carrying boxes | 1840-93 |
| 4 | Inside frame and outside cylinders | Outside | Inside | End-to-end plate | None | 1840-1960 |
| 5 | Inside frame and inside cylinders | Inside | Inside | End-to end plate | None | 1841-1950 |

[1] Other types used to a small extent included the Bury inside-cylinder inside bar frame; Forrester outside-cylinder outside-frame; and various combinations of inside and outside frames, the variety being in the location of the different axleboxes.

# 6 *Fixed Cut-off to Variable Expansion*

Actuation of the Trevithick plug cocks and Murray slide valves on the earliest locomotives was intermittent from trips on reciprocating rods and gave a single steam cut-off position in the cylinders. First move towards a rotary drive and reciprocating slide-valve motion began in 1814-15 with modifications to the Blenkinsop locomotives, but these and the later loose-eccentric motion adopted by Nicholas Wood at Killingworth still produced intermittent actuation of the valve itself. Lap was simply enough to ensure the port was covered, but the exhaust could be closed just before dead centre and the steam admitted just after dead centre, thus easing the pronounced jerky movement of the very early locomotives. It was a measure of George Stephenson's skill at the time that in his first two locomotives of 1814-15 he copied the older actuation of the valves in the Blenkinsop locomotives, whereas Matthew Murray, more experienced as a mechanical engineer, was by then altering his original method.

*Locomotion* probably was the first to have smooth and continuous movement of the slide valve derived from an eccentric. (Chapter 3). Next basic variation was the bevel mechanism in *Lancashire Witch* (1828) that was tied in to the regulator and gave a 50 per cent cut-off position as well as the full-admission stage. With *Rocket* a return was made to full cut-off only, but with the first of the real gab gears, though with gabs on the footplate by the firebox back.

*Planet* had a modification that eliminated small deep-notched gabs and transferred the valve actuating rods to the front of the cylinders, while retaining treadle operation for the sideways movement of the eccentrics to give forward or backward gear. The slide valves themselves were moved, on reversal of direction, by two curved levers at the driving position connected by long rods to the front cross rods ahead of the cylinders. These curved levers oscillated to and fro all the time the engine was in motion.

This form of valve actuation, with one eccentric per cylinder and the two combined in a sleeve assembly for lateral shifting, but with the valve operating levers transferred to the back of the cylinders, was used for some years in four-wheel Planets and six-wheel Patentees. An improvement on some engines was a long-gap reach rod that eliminated the constant oscillation of the curved levers on the footplate.

In 1835 two makers, Hawthorn and Forrester, concurrently but independently evolved mechanisms incorporating two fixed eccentrics for each cylinder. The Hawthorn 0-4-0 *Comet*'s valve actuation was based on that of a Planet, but with a shallow drop hook at the front of each eccentric rod akin to the type used for some years in Bury locomotives. The Forrester arrangement had deep full-hook ends on each eccentric rod as introduced into marine practice in 1818 with the Carmichael single-eccentric double-hook motion. No further developments were made from the *Comet* layout, whereas the deep V hooks were the basis of most of the eccentric-driven gab motions of the next few years. An advantage of the four fixed-eccentric motions was the elimination of the footplate treadle for moving the previous sliding eccentrics; but in the Hawthorn engine the two curved oscillating footplate levers for moving the valves remained.

Carmichael motion, as invented, could bring a single reversing gear and had only one eccentric per cylinder, and it could be proportioned to give suitable lap and lead in both directions of travel. As far as can be traced, this motion in locomotive work was applied only to three 0-2-4 locomotives for the Dundee & Newtyle in 1833-4, by Forrester in two 2-2-2s sold to the GJR in 1840, and to a probable complete rebuild of the GJR Patentee *Scorpion* in 1840-1 which turned it from an inside-cylinder engine to outside-cylinder. The GJR applications had a very noisy arrangement of outside vertical eccentric rods with a rocking shaft drive forward to the valves above the outside cylinders, which upset the valve events every time the axlebox moved up and down in the horns; and with the short travel and almost no lap of the time a port at either end could easily be blanked. The Cavé type of roller-and-slot reversing was embodied in the GJR engines.

Over the three years 1838-40 came numerous detail developments of four-eccentric gab motions; all had a single fixed point of cut-off. The Stephenson works adopted the Carmichael double fork and one eccentric per side late in 1835, and by the end of 1836 had begun to apply four eccentrics and one reversing gear, but with a cumbrous arrangement of levers and two separate gabs per side. Sharp Roberts may have been the first to adopt two facing gabs. In 1841 Stephenson was using a double gab attached to the intermediate valve spindle instead of to the eccentric rod, and so it could move only in a horizontal direction. This was one of the several provisions in the long-boiler patent.

By the end of 1841 the various gab motions were such that the Stephenson shifting link motion

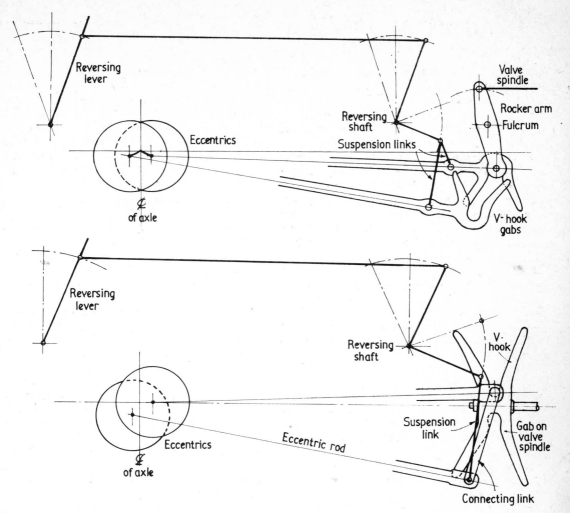

Fig 10
Top: Buddicom gab motion employing facing V hook gabs providing single fixed point cut off in forward and reverse.
Bottom: Stephenson double gab attached to valve spindle, one of the provisions of the long boiler patent

almost invented itself, for no more than normal mechanical acumen was needed among men who already were striving to improve the existing valve gears to combine the two single-hook facing gabs and common reversing gear of the Buddicom and similar motions into a single curved link. So natural was the move that the long-standing acrimony between protagonists of Williams and Howe as to which was the real inventor had no great point.

Once the two facing hooks were modified and combined into a single link the various concomitant advantages would come crowding in on locomotive designers, and probably this aspect led Robert Stephenson himself to say a short time before the first shifting link gear appeared on North Midland

long-boiler 2-4-0 No 71 at the end of 1842: 'There is no occasion to try any further at scheming valve motions. One of our people has now hit upon a plan that beats all other valve motions.' The name 'Stephenson' may have been applied almost straight away to cover any internal controversy between Williams and Howe.

The gear was not patented and Robert Stephenson himself may have had an inkling that a patent might not be valid, for this shifting link motion was not the first infinitely-variable expansion motion and not the first curved link motion; it was the first convenient one. It had been preceded by John Gray's horse-leg motion, part of his patent No 7745 of 26 July 1838, which had been applied to a rebuild of the Haigh Foundry 2-2-2 *Cyclops* of the LMR in 1839 and to several 2-2-2s and 0-6-0s on the Hull & Selby 1840-4. Later (1846-8) it was put on a dozen Hackworth-built 2-2-2s for the LBSCR. Gray's specification was, and still is today, an instructive dissertation on expansion valve motion and on the

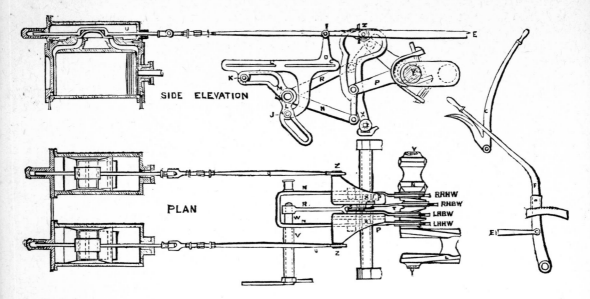

SIDE ELEVATION

PLAN

RRHW
RHBW
LHBW
LHHW

**Fig 11**
John Gray's horse-leg expansion motion applied over the years 1839-47 on the LMR, H&SR, YNMR and LBSCR. The extra handle on the right gave extra purchase on the main reversing lever in view of the weight to be shifted; found again in principle 60 years later on the Ivatt big-boiler Atlantics with foot rest on the sector-plate base

**Fig 12**
The Stephenson shifting link motion had its first application in December 1842. The gear shown here is the cumbersome indirect installation made at Crewe to standard 2-2-2 6ft engines of the Northern Division of the LNWR from 1844 to 1853. The boiler feed pump was driven by the short light rod from the backward eccentric strap.

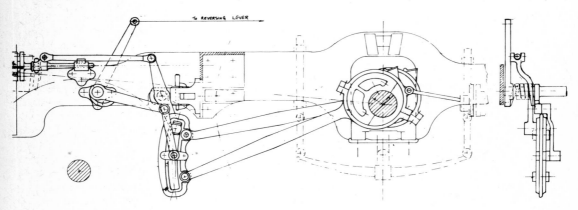

To REVERSING LEVER

functions and occurrence of lap, lead, expansion, release, compression, and even of limited cut-off.

In essence his patent was for the whole idea of infinitely-variable expansion mechanism as much as for the horse-leg type of curved link and complicated actuating gear he employed. So heavy was the motion to pull over that a detachable extra handle was provided to give the driver more leverage, an idea followed 60 years later in the Ivatt large-boiler Atlantics on the GNR, in which the driver was given a raised foot rest to get greater purchase on the big lever.

At the end of 1847, Gray began to make claims for £20 an engine fitted with Stephenson link mo-

tion, not against the Stephenson firm but against the LNWR as one of the largest users of shifting link motion, and one that was building sets of such motion in its own shops. Moreover the LNWR was the legatee of the LMR which had paid Gray a royalty for the motion on *Cyclops* and so, by inference, had accepted the validity of the patent. Obviously this was to be a test case; if Gray won he could claim royalties from all other users of Stephenson motion. Francis Trevithick, the chief at Crewe, was first ordered to report upon the matter, and then the advice of Robert Stephenson and Joseph Locke was sought. After some years of spasmodic correspondence came a preliminary hearing of an action entered at Liverpool by Gray, and then the matter was closed in 1851 by the LNWR paying Gray £5000 in full settlement of all claims, and Gray pursued the matter no further with other users or builders.

From that time Gray disappeared from the railway scene and died a year or two afterwards. But the locomotive side of the railway scene owed much to him, including the whole theory of expansion valve motions, long-lap long-travel valves, the Jenny Lind form of frame construction, boiler pressure well above the normal, high boiler pitch, high centre of gravity, and early studies of axle life. He was associated also with the first coal-burning special firebox to be tried; and it was on his repeated requests that at the end of 1832 the LMR board ordered a simple hydraulic press to force wheels on and off axles instead of continuing to use sledge hammers.

Gray's work on valve gears before he left the LMR must have led to the trials with increased lap on that railway in 1838-9. After John Dixon departed for the SDR in 1836 Edward Woods became chief engineer of the LMR and had under him Melling in charge of the locomotives. Melling was discharged early in 1840 and John Dewrance took his place; almost at the same time Gray went to the Hull & Selby. The tests of increased lap therefore have usually been known as the Woods-Dewrance trials.

These experiments were initiated because of high coke consumption. In general the Planets and Patentees had only 1/16in steam lap, that is just enough to ensure that the valve could fully cover the port. Lap on one or two engines was increased to $\frac{3}{8}$in and the valve travel correspondingly lengthened. A reduction of 20 per cent in coke consumption resulted, and when lap was increased to $\frac{3}{4}$in with corresponding increase in travel the consumption was reduced by 35 per cent of the original figure. These economies came almost entirely from the reduction in back pressure by earlier release of exhaust steam as prognosticated by Gray in July 1838, and began to have effect on the practice of other railways.

*Cyclops*, with horse-leg motion, had a travel of about 6in, a lap of $\frac{7}{8}$in and an exhaust lap of $\frac{3}{8}$in, and the range of cut-off was only from 46 to 82 per cent. LMR coke sheets for 1842 show *Cyclops* consuming 17lb/mile on passenger and goods trains; all other engines except the then new *Heron* of Dewrance's Bird class consumed 18 to 30lb/mile. On tests over the GJR between Liverpool and Birmingham with trailing loads of 50 tons *Cyclops* and the Patentee *Hecate* showed the same average consumption of 25.8lb/mile, but *Cyclops* maintained an average speed of 28mph against the 20mph of

*Hecate*. After the economy given by the simple increase in lap Woods and Dewrance would have no more horse-leg motions.

The negligible influence of Gray's original thought and work is a commentary on a pronounced aspect of British locomotive engineering from first to last: the costive reception accorded to any clear thought on fundamentals and progressive design, especially if it did not originate in the 'home' steam-tight compartment within which railway locomotive engineers soon began to seal themselves. Little more than a cursory study of Gray's specification at any time from 1840 would have shown the way to an improvement in expansion motions of all types as great as the advance those motions themselves were over the preceding gab gears. This became clearer still after Gray's mechanically cumbersome gear was replaced by the simpler shifting and stationary link forms.

D. K. Clark in 1855[32] supplemented Gray's reasoning on long lap with long travel; but Robert Sinclair was the only man to adopt the principle in those years. No real advance was made in valve and valve motion characteristics until Churchward wittingly introduced long-lap long-travel valves around 1903. His work was no more understood than was that of Gray 65 years earlier.

Long lap and long travel did not of themselves give good power performance, free running, and fuel and steam economy. Proportions and settings also had to be correct, in particular the ratio between lap and lead. Gray recognised this in 1838 and in his specification set out what he considered the desirable leads for various laps. Churchward also appreciated this to the full; indeed one often wonders whether he studied Gray's specification. He insisted that the maximum lead be small, not more than one-twelfth of the lap, and so in practice his engines could be worked successfully at short cut-offs and full regulator opening without undue compression. His prototype 4-6-0 No 98 (later 2998) had $1\frac{1}{8}$in lap, $5\frac{7}{8}$in max travel, and the $\frac{1}{8}$in lead at 25 per cent cut-off was reduced to $\frac{1}{8}$in negative lead at 77 per cent full-gear cut-off by the proportions of the Stephenson motion, which had a long expansion link and eccentric rods short in relation to the throw.

Suitable lap-lead ratios were desirable both with variable-lead gears and the fixed-lead types such as Walschaerts. Neglect of this factor is shown by the diversity of practice and by the varying standards of performance of long-lap long-travel engines on different railways. In 1910 the LNWR Experiment 4-6-0s had what for the time was the long travel of 5in, but had only 1 1/16in lap and 3/16in constant lead from Joy valve motion. One of the class, *Worcestershire*, was tried briefly against the GWR four-cylinder 4-6-0 *Polar Star* which had valve events approximating to those of GWR No 98 just mentioned, and *Worcestershire* was quite outclassed, largely on steam utilisation grounds. The LNWR four-cylinder Claughtons of 1913 were supposed to incorporate the lessons learned in the 1910 trials, but actually showed a retrogression, for the max valve travel was cut to 4 5/16in, the lap to 1.0in, and the lead was 5/32in constant from Walschaerts gear. Lead:lap ratio thus was about one-sixth.

Churchward's four-cylinder locomotives with 7in travel and $1\frac{1}{8}$in lap had a constant lead from Walschaerts motion limited to 0.11in to 0.13in in forward gear, that is one-twelfth to one-fifteenth of the lap; they were free runners and could be worked at 12 to 15 per cent cut-off and full throttle. On the SR, with travels around $6\frac{1}{2}$in and $1\frac{1}{2}$in lap the constant lead given by the Walschaerts motion in the Lord Nelsons, King Arthurs and Schools was $\frac{1}{4}$in, or one-sixth of the lap, and compression at early cut-offs was so high that the engines could hardly be linked beyond 25 per cent. Much of their work was done on 30 per cent cut-off, which meant only first port of the regulator was needed. Thus the necessary driving technique was brought back to what it was in the days of $\frac{7}{8}$in to 1in lap and $4\frac{1}{4}$in travel. The LI class 4-4-0s of 1924 were even worse,

for with Stephenson motion the $\frac{1}{8}$in lead at 78 per cent full-gear cut-off was increased to no less than $\frac{3}{8}$in (or one-third of the lap) at 25 per cent cut-off.

Gresley did not fully appreciate long travel long lap. His GNR 1000-class three-cylinder Moguls of 1920 had long-lap long-travel valves and a good setting with one-twelfth lead:lap ratio; but malfunctioning of his conjugated valve motion led him to reduce the maximum travel as an easy way out instead of dealing with the source of the trouble. By this means he came to 65 per cent maximum cut-off. After the GWR/LNER locomotive trials of 1925, Gresley resisted for 18 months the obvious required change back to long lap long travel for the Pacifics; and when he did begin to apply it he retained the limited max cut-off though the reason for this had disappeared. Nevertheless, with the one-twelfth lead:lap ratio his 180lb and 220lb Pacifics could run well at 15 per cent cut-off.

Apart from the Royal Scots on the LMSR, which arose from GWR locomotive performance in the interchange trials of 1926, Churchward's appreciation of correct ratios did not spread with intent to other systems, not even when Swindon-trained men occupied influential positions, as on the SR and, from 1932, the LMSR. Stanier provided $\frac{1}{4}$in lead for $1\frac{1}{4}$in lap in the class 5 4-6-0s and Princess Royal Pacifics,

| Table 3 Valve and Valve Motion Characteristics | | | | | | | | | |
|---|---|---|---|---|---|---|---|---|---|
| Railway and Loco | Year | Wheel arrgt | No of cyls | Motion | Max travel | Steam lap | Lead | Max cut-off | Max lead-lap ratio |
| | | | | | in | in | in | % | |
| Hull & Selby (Gray) | 1844 | 0-6-0 | 2 | Gray | 6.0 | 1.5 | 0.375 | 70 | 1:4 |
| LNWR Precursor | 1874 | 2-4-0 | 2 | Allan | 4.25 | 1.375 | 0.125 constant | 56 | 1:11 |
| LNWR Cauliflower | 1882 | 0-6-0 | 2 | Joy | 4.25 | 1.0 | 0.1875 constant | 78 | 1:5.3 |
| Highland | 1894 | 4-6-0 | 2 | Allan | 4.25 | 1.0 | 0.1875 constant | 75 | 1:5.3 |
| CR Dunalastair | 1896 | 4-4-0 | 2 | Stephenson | 4.1875 | 1.0 | 0.1875 full gear | | 1:5.3 |
| GER Claud Hamilton | 1900 | 4-4-0 | 2 | Stephenson | 3.43 | 0.875 | 0.125 full gear | 73 | 1:7 |
| LNWR Experiment | 1905 | 4-6-0 | 2 | Joy | 5.0 | 1.016 | 0.1875 constant | 78 | 1:5.7 |
| GWR No 98 | 1906 | 4-6-0 | 2 | Stephenson | 5.875 | 1.625 | 0.125 @ 25%–0.125 @ 77% | 77 | 1:13 |
| GWR Star | 1907 | 4-6-0 | 4 | Walschaerts | 6.875 | 1.625 | 0.125 constant | 76 | 1:13 |
| LNWR George V | 1911 | 4-4-0 | 2 | Joy | 5.5 | 1.25 | 0.1875 constant | 78 | 1:6.7 |
| LNWR Claughton | 1913 | 4-6-0 | 4 | Walschaerts | 4.312 | 1.00 | 0.156 constant | 82 | 1:6.4 |
| GER 1500 | 1912 | 4-6-0 | 2 | Stephenson | 4.2 | 1.125 | 0.28 @ 15%–0.14 @ 70% | 72 | 1:4 |
| GNR 1640 | 1918 | 2-6-0 | 2 | Walschaerts | 5.28 | 1.25 | 0.125 constant | 73 | 1:10 |
| SR L1 | 1924 | 4-4-0 | 2 | Stephenson | 5.56 | 1.1875 | 0.38 @ 20%–0.125 @ 78% | 78 | 1:3.1 |
| LNER A4 | 1935 | 4-6-2 | 3 | Walschaerts | 5.75 | 1.625 | 0.125 constant | 65 | 1:13 |
| LMSR Coronation | 1937 | 4-6-2 | 4 | Walschaerts | 7.03 | 1.75 | 0.0625 constant | 75 | 1:28 |
| GWR Hall | 1930 | 4-6-0 | 2 | Stephenson | 6.91 | 1.75 | 0.16 @ 15%–0.17 @ 77% | 82 | 1:11 |
| SR Merchant Navy | 1941 | 4-6-2 | 3 | Bulleid Walschaerts | 6.1 | 1.625 | 0.125 constant | 70 | 1:13 |
| BR Britannia | 1952 | 4-6-2 | 2 | Walschaerts | 7.73 | 1.69 | 0.25 | 79 | 1:6.8 |

and only in the Coronation streamlined Pacifics did he come to 1/16in lead for the same lap. Thus 90 years after Gray the principles he enunciated had not been fully assimilated on British railways.

Stephenson shifting link motion ousted the gab types overnight for new construction in England, but the latter continued to run in decreasing numbers through the 1850s when duties and conditions of fitted engines did not warrant the expense of a rebuild. The 1862 stock list of the LNWR showed three gab-fitted engines still in being, and one gab-fitted colliery locomotive was at work in 1909. Freedom in running was as much part of the link motion's attributes as were economy in fuel and water. Locke told the Gauge Commissioners in August 1845 that one of the new Crewe-type engines (it would be a 6ft 2-2-2) had just been timed at 57mph, and spoke of this as being a high figure, as indeed it was for the time.

Observing the construction and results of the shifting link motion, Daniel Gooch in 1844 devised the stationary link form in which the reversing gear moved the radius rod up and down instead of the link as in the Stephenson type. This meant the link was concave to the slide valve instead of to the eccentrics; also the lead remained constant instead of increasing as the gear was linked up. These differences were not important in those days, but in later years the variable lead was an advantage when over 300rpm became an accepted figure in everyday service for link-motion engines. Gooch did not patent the gear; according to his diaries he had too much trouble with his 1840 patent for steel tyres (see Chapter 8) to take out any further patents. Several locomotive makers such as Hawthorn made wide, though not exclusive, use of this motion up to about 1865, and such celebrated engines as the *Plews* and the Conner 8ft 2in singles had it.

Third of the great link motions was that devised and patented in 1855 by Alexander Allan while locomotive superintendent of the Scottish Central, and applied first to two SCR 0-4-2 goods engines in 1856. The feature was a straight link that was easier to machine. In linking up or reversing both the link and die block on one hand and the intermediate valve spindle on the other were moved, in opposite directions. Thus by suitable proportioning of the reversing shaft arms the moments of the two groups could be made to balance each other so that no balance weight or spring on the reversing shaft was needed. Only a slight increase in lead occurred when linking up.

From old records Allan appears to have received £5 an engine royalty, and for 40 years the motion was much used on the LNWR and Highland, and also in such engines as the Met and District 4-4-0Ts. Many of the applications came after the patent

rights had expired, and the gear was applied in decreasing quantities in new construction until 1917.

Early link-motion applications often were complicated by the low boiler pitch which made underslung reversing shafts and low hung gears common, and at times led to complex indirect drives such as found in Crewe-built engines from 1844 to 1851. These motions also were well suited to direct (ie non-rocking shaft) drives, and the possibilities for these were increased substantially by Robert Stephenson's patent No 8998 of 23 June 1841 which, additional to long-boiler locomotives, covered the position of the slide valves between a pair of inside cylinders with faces either vertical or at an angle. This feature soon became a constructional standard, but Stephenson does not appear to have drawn any royalties, though such were collected on long-boiler locomotives from other makers who built to Stephenson drawings.

At the time, with small cylinders and low pressures, this location was a happy thought, but its retention to the bitter end led to a restriction in effective power output as cylinders grew larger and pressures higher. In one batch of locomotives or another were to be found valve positions all round the cylinder: inside, below, outside, on top, parallel, sloped up, sloped down, and at an angle on the inside.

Practical radial gears began with the nearly concurrent invention of Walschaerts motion in Belgium and Heusinger gear in Germany. Neither in its original form was like the so-called Walschaerts motion applied for a century and more, and which combined the leading features of the two, though Heusinger von Waldegg's name was perpetuated only in German literature. Walschaerts' original invention, though it combined one variable and one invariable motion, did not have fixed lead, and the link, derived from Crampton's motion of 1842,[33] was concave to the axle. It was, in fact, an inferior mechanism to the existing link motions. By the time it was adopted in England the gear had developed to the form it retained to the end of steam, with a rotary drive for the oscillating motion of the expansion link giving the normal movement to the slide valve, plus a lap-and-lead movement derived from the reciprocating motion of the crosshead. Lead was constant, and the cylinder events of compression and release were as good as those given by link motions.

First use on an English railway was in an outside-cylinder 0-6-6-0 Fairlie on the East & West Junction Railway in 1876, an engine built some time previously by the Yorkshire Engine Co for Mexico and left on the builder's hands. Second application was to the outside-cylinder Fairlie

0-4-4T on the Swindon, Marlborough & Andover Junction Railway in 1878; so to R. F. Fairlie himself is probably due some of the credit for having appreciated the merits of this motion. No further installations were made until the Belfast & Northern Counties began to use it in 1890 for two-cylinder compounds, which had inside cylinders and inside motion. Probably Bowman Malcolm, the engineer, was influenced and encouraged in this by Beyer Peacock, who built his engines.

Otherwise little notice of the motion was taken by English railways until the production of large 4-4-2 and 4-6-0 locomotives in the dozen years before World War I; then it came not through normal development but from a new foreign influence, the French de Glehn compound Atlantic No 102 bought by the GWR in 1903. Until 1914 Walschaerts motion was applied almost entirely to multi-cylinder locomotives such as the Star series of 4-6-0s on the GWR from 1906; the three GNR compound Atlantics Nos 292, 1300 and 1421 in 1905-7; the GCR three-cylinder simple rebuild of Atlantic No 1090 in 1909; and the LNWR four-cylinder 4-6-0 Claughtons in 1913.

Lightness rather than improvement in steam distribution was the reason for the resuscitation, for eccentrics were getting very heavy and big enough to cause a lot of friction and absorb much power to drive them. This became a talking point when long valve travels were desired, as on the GWR; nevertheless Churchward perpetuated eccentric drive for his four-cylinder engines, and accepted two large eccentrics in place of four; but his was the only inside Walschaerts motion of those years. All others were outside and had the simple flycrank drive.

Joy's motion was the favourite radial type in Britain for 30 years after its first use in 1879, thanks largely to the influence of F. W. Webb and Crewe not only on the LNWR but on the locomotive superintendents of the LYR (Aspinall, Hoy and Hughes) and on T. W. Worsdell, the ex-Crewe works manager in his time on the GER and NER. It was used on hundreds of LNWR engines built under Webb, Whale, Bowen Cooke and Beames. Universally adopted on Aspinall's inside-cylinder 4-4-2, 4-4-0, 0-6-0 and 2-4-2T classes on the LYR, it was applied also by Hughes to his four-cylinder 4-6-0s in 1909, which had two inside sets of Joy motion and rocking shaft drive to the outside valves.

Theoretically a derivation from J. W. Hackworth's radial motion of 1859, the Joy gear had an expansion link driven from near mid-length of the connecting rod. This proved the weak point that led eventually to the gear being abandoned for new construction, for as piston thrusts and wheel rpm increased the stresses round the jack-pin hole in the main rod became too great. Many rods had to be replaced because of flaws round the pin hole, and a number fractured in service with great consequential damage. Another defect was that up and down movement of the axle on the springs moved the valve slightly. The gear was light, simple and cheap to make, which was why Webb took it up. Steam distribution normally was good, and with careful setting lead and cut-off could be almost equal at each end more or less throughout the expansion range. Lead was constant.

At least 35 forms of valve motion were applied through the 160 years of British steam locomotive building without including all the old plug-cock and gab variations and the several poppet-valve types installed from 1923 onwards. Apart from the five already described (Stephenson, Gooch, Allan, Walschaerts, Joy) none was used to any extent. Some, such as the little-known Marshall, Isaacson and Bryce-Douglas types, were tried only on one or two engines. Churchward used a gear derived from a Stevart revision of a Hackworth design patented in 1849 in his four-cylinder 4-4-2 North Star in 1906 and so did R. M. Deeley in the 10 two-cylinder simple 4-4-0s of class 990 on the Midland in 1907; Hunslet applied it to an export order in the late 19th Century.

Through the Group era (1923-48) with one important exception Walschaerts motion was universal for outside-cylinder and multi-cylinder piston-valve locomotives, and even was used for inside-cylinder types like the LMS 0-8-0s of class 7F. The exception was the large number of GWR two-cylinder 4-6-0s, 2-8-0s and other formations in which Stephenson motion and rocking shafts gave a valve travel up to 7.2in and the motion arrangement was essentially that used by Churchward from 1903. Stephenson motion also was continued through those years for inside-cylinder types, mainly 0-6-0 and 0-6-0T layouts, and was used occasionally for outside cylinders when pre-Group designs were continued, as in the Tilbury 4-4-2Ts built for the LMS.

Until the late 1850s gab gears and link motions were reversed by hand levers with coarse-tooth sectors. Then Ramsbottom evolved a practical hand-screw system which was put on the DX 0-6-0s and later engines. In 1860-1 the Stephenson works produced a peculiar cigar-shaped screw to effect linking-up that had an over-riding lever for use when a direct reverse was needed. It can be seen today on the old long-boiler 0-6-0 No 1275 of the NER in York railway museum. Gradually more teeth were cut in the sector plate of lever reverse mechanisms, but by the beginning of this century were useless, for engines had become so big that drivers ran great risk in trying to make adjustments in cut-off when running at speed, and so the practice rose of stabilising cut-off early in the run and then working on the regulator.

The Group era was also the time of conjugated valve motions, for additional to the drive of four piston valves from two sets of motion in four-cylinder engines (the simplest of all conjugated systems) Gresley on the LNER obtained the movement for the inside valve in three-cylinder locomotives by an arrangement of interconnected levers from the spindles of the two outside valves, themselves actuated by Walschaerts motion. Introduced by Gresley on the GNR 2-8-0 coal engine No 461 in 1918 with cross levers in the rear of the cylinders, when the mechanism was moved to the front in the 2-6-0s of the 1000-class in 1920 to get greater accessibility it showed the defect of over-travel of the centre valve. An increase in pin diameter and in scantlings of the levers might well have minimised the troubles.

As used on the LNER the Gresley patent conjugated motion had two further defects. Owing to the steep slope needed for the inside cylinder with all three drives concentrated on the second axle, and the necessary relative locations of the piston valves, the inside valve had to be alongside its cylinder, and so its diameter was limited by the distance between frames, and the larger the cylinder the smaller the possible piston-valve size. Secondly, this valve gear arrangement was so personal a factor to Gresley that it gave him a blind spot in relation to basic valve motion characteristics and practical day by day performance.

Other Group three-cylinder classes such as the LMS Royal Scots and SR Schools had three separate sets of Walschaerts motion with eccentric drive for the inside set, though Maunsell tried one

Fig 13
Eccentric driven inside Walschaerts valve motion for inside piston valve of LMSR three-cylinder 2-6-4T, 1934

2-6-4T with conjugated drive brought forward to the front of the cylinders from the tops of the outside combination levers. This was due to Maunsell's assistant H. Holcroft. Despite an invention by David Joy,[34] and conjugated applications from other engineers in Germany from 1913, Holcroft is to be regarded as both the father and the foster-father of conjugated motions in the United Kingdom. He evolved the whole theory prior to 1914 and then worked out combinations for three- and four-cylinder engines with different crank arrangements, all based on the idea of combining two almost harmonic motions into a third with the same characteristics.

With few exceptions four-cylinder simple-expansion locomotives in Britain from Manson's 4-4-0 on the GSWR in 1897 had two sets of motion and rocking shaft drive. The exceptions included Drummond's uncoupled 4-2-2-0s of 1897-1900 which had Stephenson motion for the inside valves and an inverted form of Joy motion for the outside valves. The same engineer's 4-6-0 No 335 on the LSWR had Stephenson motion inside and Walschaerts motion outside, but his later 4-6-0s had two outside sets of Walschaerts motion with rocking shafts to the inside spindles, a reversal of Churchward's layout on the GWR, but one followed much later by Stanier in one of his Princess Royal Pacifics, and in all his Coronation Pacifics.

The early use of single and double D slide valves has been mentioned in Chapter 4. Almost coincident with the abandonment of the double valve on the LMR came attempts at piston valves. One, by Robert Stephenson & Co, was an outside-admission valve of 4in diameter for a 12in cyclinder, and apparently had four segments in two rings for each head. It was of the type used nearly a century later with a long spindle and short straight steam passages to the cylinders. A set of these valves ac-

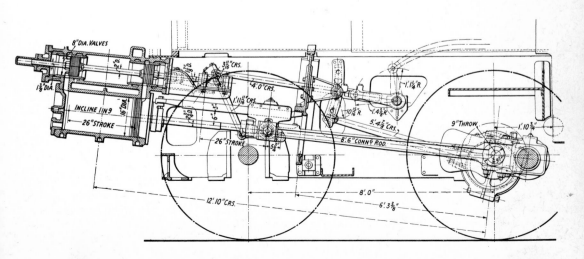

tually ran a short time on an LMR locomotive. The undated fully-dimensioned drawing says 'for Liverpool Loco'; the only LMR engines with the given 12in by 16in cylinder size were *Atlas*, *Milo* and *Pluto* of 1832.

The second type, invented by Richard Roberts in 1832, was applied to the Sharp Roberts locomotive *Experiment* in 1833, to three engines by the same builder for the Dublin & Kingstown in 1835, and to three broad-gauge 2-2-2s ordered by Brunel in 1837 for the GWR. This valve was of internal-admission type without packing rings, and operation was by short vertical arms fixed on the radius rods of the parallel motion.

Neither of these valves was successful, because materials and methods of sealing were inadequate; nor were the solid brass valves by William Bouch on the SDR 4-4-0s of 1872 because of binding. Not until the introduction of W. M. Smith's valves in 1888 did any satisfactory piston valve come on the market. Here an assembly of collapsible segments permitted entrapped water to escape, and one spring ring for sealing was fitted to each head. An automatic steam and air valve destroyed the vacuum in the steam chest when the engine was coasting.

Hundreds of these valves were fitted on the NER and Midland between 1888 and 1903 and they gave satisfactory sealing with saturated steam up to 200psi, but pressure rises above that figure and the introduction of superheated steam from 1906 brought different conditions. Churchward used the American semi-plug type with reasonable results in conjunction with his medium-temperature superheat. With above 200°F of superheat something other was required in sealing. Partly because of the early adoption of the Schmidt single broad ring, a fully satisfactory method was not forthcoming until at length multi-rings of normal Ramsbottom pattern were adopted in 1926-7 on the LNER and in 1928-9 on the LMS. This solved the problem of superheated steam leakage that had ruined the performance of almost every British engine with high superheat.

Prevalence of inside cylinders with a common valve chest between prevented much use of balanced slide valves. Those applied, as on the Aspinall engines of the LYR from 1888 and on some GNR engines later were above the cylinders; those fitted to outside cylinders were either inside the frames as on the GNR Atlantics or above the cylinders as in the first batch of LYR four-cylinder 4-6-0s (1908). In the GNR Atlantics exhaust went out the back of the valve and by a short direct passage to the blast pipe, and in this respect followed the balanced slide valve proposed by Robert Stephenson & Co in 1832.

Whatever the valves, many engines over many years suffered from ports that were too small to let out the exhaust easily. Particularly with inside cylinders having vertical-face valves between, the passages between cylinder and port face were tortuous, impeding outward steam flow and increasing clearance volume. The originator of better ratios was Drummond on the Caledonian from 1884. His successors, Lambie and McIntosh, carried on in similar fashion, and this was one reason for the fine performance of Caledonian engines in the 1895 race to Aberdeen and of the Dunalastairs on normal express trains from 1896. Drummond reverted briefly to the old Planet-type of double slide valve in 1889 to reduce steam passage length and clearance volume; but with cylinders of 18in and more in diameter the total slide valve weight increased by 70 per cent and led to expenditure of more power in driving the valves and greater wear on motion pins.

Trick-ported (ie double-ported) piston valves put forward by the Schmidt Superheater Co were installed in the superheated George V-class 4-4-0s on the LNWR in 1910 and were used in other engines later, but were the answer neither to inflow nor outflow. The Trick idea was reversed on the LMS to give a double outflow to exhaust in conjunction with short travel, and over 200 engines including the 33 LMS Beyer-Garratts were so fitted, but again this was not the answer.

Poppet valve gears were developed by the Group companies to get larger ports and passages, quick port opening and closing, less power consumption and, above all, to separate inlet and exhaust events so that, while fixed, they were independent of each other. In essence the two categories were: (1) the OC or oscillating-cam type in which the valves were actuated by Walschaerts, Stephenson or other conventional gear; and (2) the RC or rotary-cam form in which the drive was by bevels and rotating shafts from an axle or flycrank. Caprotti, Dabeg, and some of the Lentz and Franklin types were RC. The OC types had interdependent valve events as given by the motion used; the RC types eliminated the interdependence of link and radial motions but substituted another set of fixed events, and usually only a limited number of fixed cut-off points was provided by separate cams.

Caprotti gear, which showed constant lead and constant compression, gave excellent results when applied to two poor-performing four-cylinder 4-6-0s, the ex-LNWR Claughtons and ex-GCR Lord Faringdons; in modified form it was applied again in late LMS days to 20 good two-cylinder class 5 4-6-0s. In the last-named installation, instead of one complete turn of the cab handwheel that brought the earlier Caprottis from full forward to full backward, the same number of turns was provided as in the normal Walschaerts installations. Another

30 class 5 4-6-0s were so fitted in BR days, as was the class 8 Pacific *Duke of Gloucester*.

Many more applications were made of Lentz gear in Group days, beginning with an ex-GER 0-6-0 in 1925 on the LNER and extended to 17 of the ex-GER 1500-class 4-6-0s, of which 10 were built new in 1928. All these had Stephenson motion. Of the three-cylinder 4-4-0 Shire Hunt class the first batch had piston valves; the next six were given OC gear and Walschaerts motion, and the next 42 had RC gear with seven fixed cut-off positions. Two ex-NER three-cylinder Atlantics also got Lentz installations.

Gresley's first 2-8-2 passenger engine *Cock o' the North* of 1934 had rotary-cam poppet valves, at first with infinitely-variable cut-off; but trouble with the cams soon led to fixed cut-offs of 12, 18, 25, 35, 45 and 75 per cent. Then the experiment was abandoned and the five following 2-8-2s appeared with piston valves and Walschaerts motion, to which *Cock o' the North* was converted in 1938. Only LMS application of Lentz valves was to five Horwich Crab 2-6-0s in 1931-2, with RC drive and a fixed number of cut-offs. These engines ran so fitted until 1953.

Eventually a variable-lead RC gear was devised by Reidinger, and known as the RR, that eliminated the small number of fixed cut-off stages of the RC gears, and gave the possibility of making (in the running shed) independent adjustment of the pre-admission, release and compression for any given cut-off. For the first time in a steam locomotive independent and almost infinite variations of those three events for infinitely-variable cut-off could be made and the effects observed.

This gear was applied by BR in 1949 to a Hunt-class 4-4-0 No 62764 that previously had RC Lentz gear. The rebuilt engine was tested on Rugby plant and then run for three or four years in passenger service. A revised form of this RR motion was put in 1953 on to the five Horwich Crab 2-6-0s previously fitted with Lentz RC gear, but four of these were set to give predetermined fixed events, and only the fifth was given finely-adjustable cams so that the other events could be altered independently. But the day of steam development was then closing; at the end, the valve gears used in general were those introduced 120 years before. Though successful piston valves had replaced flat-D slide valves, the cylinder and valve events were within just those limitations enforced by the first variable-expansion motions of 1838-42.

# 7  From Coke to Coal

Within the Liverpool & Manchester Railway Act[35] of 1826 was a smoke-consuming clause which made coke essential as fuel in place of the coal hitherto universal on the colliery lines and on the newly-opened SDR, where with single-flue and return-flue boilers temperatures and efficiencies were low and much dirty smoke was produced. Coke as fuel eliminated smoke from the chimney top, but did not reduce the emission of sparks or the line-side fires common on the SDR. In fact, sparks projected by the strong blast setting fire to uncovered bales of cotton in the wagons, and ruining clothes of passengers in the open-top 'Blue trains' were a constant source of trouble to the LMR in its early years. Many locomotives had wire netting over the chimney top and often some kind of spark arrester in the smokebox; in addition the LMR, GJR and LNWR fitted vertical wire-mesh screens on the tender backs to try and catch sparks and ash before they descended on to and into the coaches.

Experiments with coal conducted on the LMR in 1836 on engines *Patentee* and *Star* showed consumption of screened coal was 25 per cent more than that of coke and the smoke nuisance remained. Coincident with this work the Bury engine *Liver* was fitted with the first of the numerous double fireboxes that were a well-publicised feature of main-line locomotive practice until the 1860s. This was the Chanter type, patented in September 1834, with which John Gray associated himself when trials were made on the LMR. It had a horizontal midfeather dividing the box into two; the upper grate was fed with coke and the lower one with coal; grate bars were formed of water tubes. Fuel was around three-quarters coal and one-quarter coke, and Edward Woods reported that smoke production was mitigated. Half coke and half coal might have given still better results, but in January 1837 one of the water-tube grate bars burst and injured the driver and fireman. In April the engine was again at work, but with a firebox divided vertically. However, the LMR board was reluctant to go on; Chanter was willing to buy *Liver* for £500 and continue his experiments elsewhere, but the board wanted more, and in October 1837 sold the engine to a contractor for £700.

From 1841 until well on in the 20th Century many trials were made with air inlets through the firebox side, sometimes with steam entraining jets. Principal early sponsor of this method was D. K. Clark, and in 1858-60 he made trials on the North London, Eastern Counties, and Great North of Scotland (GNSR) railways with air inlets totalling about 4sq in per sq ft of grate area. On the GNSR Clark's side inlets with steam jets were used on all main-line engines built from 1860 to 1880; succeeding engines until around 1890 had the air inlets transferred to the throat and back plates and the steam jets were given up. All engines ran without brick arches as long as they retained the air holes. In 1862 William Cowan, the GNSR locomotive superintendent, wrote:[36] '... smoke consumption is a fact accomplished really and truly; its application as a damper while standing is a feature peculiar to this system alone ... and it is used here daily for that purpose.'

John Dewrance, while still in charge of LMR locomotives, evolved a firebox with vertical or sloping midfeather dividing the box transversely. The front portion had no grate bars and was considered as a combustion chamber, but both back and front portions had ashpan dampers. The two portions were connected multitubular fashion. This box was tried in 1845-6 between Liverpool and Birmingham in the 2-2-2 *Condor*, built to normal construction a year or two before; but with the take-over of the LMR by the GJR in 1845 and then the fusion of the latter into the LNWR in 1846 no promotion was given Dewrance and the experiments lapsed. Dewrance always claimed[37] that the later and better-known Beattie firebox was really his, and that he had sent drawings to Joseph Beattie and permitted him to use them.

One factor preventing success with early attempts at coal burning was the small firebox size, which had grown up on the basis of coke fuel. The volume was too restricted to give space or time for proper mixing of the incoming air and the coal, and there was a direct short path from firebed to tubes. This was particularly so in long-boiler locomotives which were wrongly proportioned for coal to an even greater degree than ordinary six-wheelers. Even coke burning in such engines was not always a simple matter, for a coke fire could not be allowed to run well down, as it could not be blown up again as could a coal fire. In fact, the blower as such only came in with coal firing.

Beattie's, McConnell's and Cudworth's were the principal forms of special fireboxes applied through the 1850s and 1860s to produce smoke-free coal burning. All three patentees showed tenacity in continuing construction after the non-patented brick arch and firehole deflector plate were proved equally efficient, simpler, and easier for firing. In all, a larger grate area was realised to be necessary with coal, and the forms evolved were intended to

Table 4  Evaporation of Early Locomotive Boilers

| Locomotive | Year | Type of boiler and firebox | Evap hs sq ft | Grate area sq ft | Hourly evaporation lb | Hourly fuel consumption lb | Unit evaporation lb/lb coal |
|---|---|---|---|---|---|---|---|
| Killingworth  0-4-0 | 1825 | Single flue | 42 | 7.0 | 1000 | 300[1] | 3.3 |
| Sanspareil  0-4-0 | 1829 | Return flue | 90 | 10.0 | 1500 | 690[2] | 2.17 |
| Rocket  0-2-2 | 1829 | Multitubular[3] | 138 | 6.0 | 1140 | 214[2] | 5.35 |
| Bury (LBR)  0-4-0 | 1838 | Multitubular[4] | 461 | 9.2 | 5300 | 1010[2] | 5.25 |
| Midland No 54 [5] | 1846 | Multitubular | 903[5] | 9.6 | 9400 | 940[2] | 10.0 |
| MSL Sphynx  0-6-0[5] | 1847 | Multitubular | 952[5] | 10.6 | 14000 | 1550[2] | 9.0 |
| LSWR Snake  2-2-2 | 1848 | Multitubular | 898 | 12.4 | 9450 | 1080[2] | 8.75 |
| GWR Iron Duke  4-2-2[6] | 1848 | Multitubular | 1769 | 21.0 | 14350 | 1720[2] | 8.33 |
| LNWR Bloomer  2-2-2 | 1853 | Multitubular | 1294 | 18.7 | 6500 | 960[2] | 6.75 |

[1] Coal          [2] Coke          [3] Separate firebox
[4] Haycock firebox     [5] Long-boiler locomotive     [6] Broad gauge

get more firebox evaporative surface and to provide greater intermixing of air with the fuel and primary products of combustion. Other forms of box also were evolved, such as the Hawthorn, Allan and Longridge & Richardson, but they had only the slightest application.

Extraordinary shapes were used by Beattie and McConnell. Both made use of divided boxes with combustion chambers in front, but Beattie's boxes were divided into upper and lower halves leading to backward and forward sections of the grate, and the firedoors were one above the other, whereas McConnell's box was divided longitudinally and the firedoors were alongside one another. In both cases small-bore (down to $1\frac{1}{8}$in) tubes ran from the front of the combustion chamber to the smokebox tubeplate, and sometimes 300 and more were packed into a 4ft barrel. When McConnell began his trials in 1852-3 on the Southern Division of the LNWR he was already becoming a leader of the big-engine policy and some of his engines had 22sq ft of grate. Beattie continued to apply such boxes to LSWR locomotives until the mid-1870s, but from the early 1850s his keynote was thermal efficiency and his special boilers were supplemented by feedwater heating.

Around 1859-60 Beyer Peacock took out a licence from Beattie and prevailed on several railways to try a firebox. They rarely tried more than one, and usually took that one out as soon as possible. Beyer even persuaded Patrick Stirling, of all people, to try one on a GSWR 2-4-0 goods engine, and even got him to sponsor a paper[38] in which he said the box had run 25,000 miles on trains of 200 to 250 tons at an average coal consumption of 37.5lb/mile. Nevertheless he fitted no more.

Cudworth's system was a little simpler than the other two for no combustion chamber was used. The firebox was long, and for seven-eighths of its length was divided by a vertical midfeather. Each side of the box had a fire hole fired alternately. The grate sloped steeply from back to front; the fireman simply tipped the coal in through the fire doors and let it work its own way forward, burning gradually in the process. Firebox life tended to be longer than with the Beattie and McConnell types, so much so that some worked for a dozen years after Cudworth's retirement.

Only the enormous potential savings, taking the country's railways as a whole, that would result from the general substitution of coal for coke, led railway directors to sanction the expense of these special boxes, for a total change-over to coal could add $\frac{1}{4}$ to $\frac{1}{2}$ per cent on the annual dividend; but from such things they were eventually delivered by the combination of the brick arch and iron or steel firehole deflector plate in fireboxes of volume and grate area proportioned to coal.

Probably feeling instinctively that a satisfactory method within four walls of a square box would have to come, Matthew Kirtley on the Midland supported for some years the researches of his assistant Charles Markham (later head of the Staveley Coal & Iron Co) who by 1858-9 had shown that in all normal boxes a long up-sloping firebrick arch plus a long down-sloping firehole deflector plate – both unpatentable and without fees attached – would so mix air and fuel products, and increase the length and time of air passage between grate bars and entering the tubes, that smoke would be eliminated for all practical purposes, though only strict attention to regulations would prevent smoke just where it was most inadmissible, that is when standing in passenger terminals in big towns. By 1860

Markham was able in the design stage to ensure satisfactory results. With Kirtley's concurrence the results and data were given to any who might want them, even before Markham presented a comprehensive paper.[39] A valuable practical part of the Midland work was the introduction of the simple lever-operated divided sliding firedoor.

Of equal potential in handling coal fires, though a potential not realised in British practice for 80 years, was the rocking grate of Jeffreys on the Shrewsbury & Hereford, introduced with coal burning in 1856, so that the firebed could be shaken at any time. It had other advantages which were described[40] as: 'An engine run from Shrewsbury to Hereford could be taken over a pit, drop her fire, have the whole of the clinker removed, and be ready to start with a clean fire in quarter of an hour.'

For the various systems and boxes outlined above C. J. T. Young gave[41] fuel consumptions in lb/ton-mile on passenger trains of 100-120 tons weight of: McConnell 0.31, Beattie 0.235 Cudworth, 0.225, Douglas 0.32, Yarrow 0.26, Conner 0.26, Clark 0.19. As a measure of the progress, Killingworth engines in 1825 had consumption of 1.6lb/ton-mile of coal.

Most important of all other variations was Ramsbottom's two 7in-square air holes, covered by dampers, in the throatplate that admitted air under a short arch down-sloping to the back. This was introduced on the LNWR in 1859 after Birmingham Corporation had threatened a fine of £2 a day for each locomotive producing smoke in its area. Ramsbottom applied these holes to many hundreds of engines through the rest of his time on the LNWR, but after 1860 the grates were horizontal and the brick arch sloped up to the back. Webb eliminated these air holes within a year or two.

Shrewsbury & Hereford 2-4-0 long-boiler locomotive with Gothic firebox; this locomotive would be one of those fitted with drop grates 1856-60.

Though the introduction of ample combustion air for coal burning was thus effected, through the remaining 100 years of steam locomotives there was no agreement as to how much air was best. For any type of coal the maximum clear width between firebars had to be selected carefully, but at the time of the 1923 Grouping the total air space through the bars as a percentage of the grate area was 25 on the Caledonian, 33 on the GSWR, 33 on the NBR, 35 on the NER, 25 on the LNWR, 35 to 40 on the Midland, 45 on the GER, and 37 on the GNR. After some years Gresley made a big improvement by increasing the ratio to about 55 per cent on LNER main-line engines, though later some reduction was made; and on the SR Pacifics in 1941 Bulleid followed his old chief in providing 50 per cent. BR, however, went back to 36 per cent for large main-line locomotives like the Britannia Pacifics and class 9 2-10-0s.

Despite the success and simplicity of the Midland principles the midfeather died hard when not associated with special-box construction, and the vertical type was applied to various locomotives on the GNR, NER, GWR, LBSCR, SDR and LSWR through the 1850s and 1860s. Patrick Stirling tried a midfeather in the shape and location of a brick arch in the second and third of his 8ft single-drivers, Nos 8 and 33 of 1870-1; this was not repeated, for it was contrary to the natural rise of hot water. One further attempt with complete combustion chamber was made when GER 0-6-0 No 492 ran in 1879-80 with the American Weston type. It was equal in complication to a Beattie, and provided the first taper or wagon-top boiler in England. Second wagon-top application was in 1884 to three 0-6-0Ts on the Taff Vale, to ensure the firebox crown was always covered with water when working on the 1 in 13 Pwllyrhebog incline.

All these constructions were merely variations of the multitubular boiler with internal firebox built first in 1830 to burn coke, but which in its time

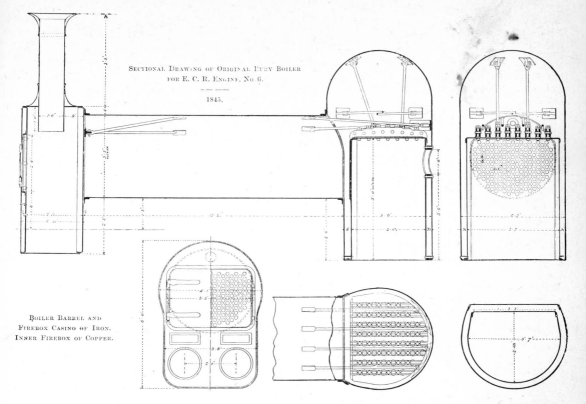

SECTIONAL DRAWING OF ORIGINAL BURY BOILER
FOR E. C. R. ENGINE, No. 6.
———
1845.

BOILER BARREL AND
FIREBOX CASING OF IRON.
INNER FIREBOX OF COPPER.

Fig 14
Bury cylindrical firebox with hemispherical top as
applied to four-wheelers 1840-5; coke burning. Large
rectangular smokebox door covering all tube area;
inside box copper.

burned coal of varying grades down to 30 per cent
ash, anthracite dust, pulverised coal, wood, turf,
bagasse, crude oil, tar oil, and colloidal mixtures.
Departures from this princple were few and unim-
portant. The water-tube boilers and fireboxes tried
from time to time, such as the Yarrow boiler on
LNER No 10000, were not such a good backbone
for the whole locomotive.

Nor did water tubes across the firebox, beginning
with Hackworth's *Globe* on the SDR in 1830 and
ending with Drummond's arrangement in the 20th
Century, ever prove worthwhile; but with big strides
in metallurgy and welding processes the use of arch
tubes from throat plate to back plate, and of thermic
syphons from throatplate to crown, became common
practice with steel fireboxes (eg the Bulleid Pacifics
in this country), and were even acceptable occasionally in copper boxes (Gresley's *Bantam Cock*
of 1941).

Though the thermic syphon gave intensified
water circulation and increased the high-production
evaporative surface, a principal advantage was that
it kept the crown covered even with low or no water
in the gauge glass. This was almost as crucial a

point in hard-worked locomotives in the last 30
years of steam as it had been under the primitive
and unskilled driving of the first 30 years.

By the time of the special fireboxes the shape of
the outer firebox had resettled to that of *Planet*
from the curious intermediate stages that began
with the circular boxes of Bury in 1830-1 and
progressed to the haycock and gothic shapes which
extended far above the boiler tops to give adequate
steam space and to house the dry pipe entry well
above water level. Bury's idea had been to get a
stayless circular firebox, but George Stephenson, as
engineer of the LMR, scotched that at once when
*Liver* was ready for that railway. Nevertheless,
well-stayed circular boxes remained Bury practice
for 15 years and were put on from time to time by
other makers, often with a great domed top encased
in polished copper.

In the Stephenson long-boiler locomotives the
four sides of the square box were prolonged upwards
to a blunt central point some 24in above the top of
the barrel, hence the name 'Gothic'. This needed
more staying than semi-circular or haystack tops. In
new construction these boxes did not extend beyond
1850, but a round top raised a few inches beyond
the barrel was used on many locomotives for the
remainder of the 19th Century, and in the
flat-top Belpaire form was built even into this century in the GWR City-class 4-4-0s and others.

First locomotive to run in Britain with a Belpaire firebox was MSLR 0-6-2T No 7 (later GCR No 515) in 1891, but the box had been applied to export orders from 1872 when Beyer Peacock put them on two 2-4-0s with Beattie fireboxes for the Malines-Terneuzen Railway. Before that again, a flat-top box had been put by William Bouch onto one class of long-boiler 0-6-0 on the SDR and had the unusual feature that the top of the box was an inch or two *below* the top of the barrel. None of these firebox tops came for combustion reasons; they were attempts to gain greater steam space and drier steam, and in the cases of the Belpaire and SDR boxes to get easier construction and more effective staying even at the expense of rather greater weight.

Many early inside fireboxes were of iron, and some lasted well; but there was a tendency to blister and copper gradually became the accepted material. This made the inside box and its copper side stays the most expensive constituent in the locomotive, and with gradual increase in steel production attempts were made to use that material, often in special shapes such as the corrugated square and cylindrical boxes of Webb from 1889, and the corrugated circular flues of Hoy on the LYR. Normal steel boxes were installed from time to time as in 11 small 0-6-0Ts on the GER in 1888-93; but neither these nor the more special types were handled with perseverance and understanding.

Steel soon became the standard material in North America and elsewhere, but copper was retained in Britain until Bulleid adopted steel with electric welding, and introduced thermic syphons, in the Merchant Navy Pacifics in 1941 largely to save weight. Steel was not adopted by BR, the given reason being that water quality differed too much throughout the country and would have led to corrosion and cracking. This was so only if water treatment, universal in North America, was not applied. Bulleid eventually adopted it on the SR and his steel fireboxes then became most successful.

A major step in British firebox construction came with the wide box of Ivatt's big-boiler Atlantic in 1902 and the concurrent adoption of a similar shape in the notorious GER 0-10-0T. These were not Wootten boxes as often claimed in their early years, for that American box was shallow and of extreme width designed to burn anthracite dust at a very low firing rate and with small relative firebox volume. In conjunction with the 5ft 6in dia barrel, this box in GNR No 251 and its followers produced a boiler of great steaming capacity and ample water reserve. Grate area was some 15 per cent more than in the largest narrow box of the period, but the firebox heating surface was some 15 per cent less.

Such a box needed a trailing carrying axle,

though it did not get it in the small-wheel GER 0-10-0T. Despite its simplicity and effectiveness it was applied to only one other British Atlantic class, the LBSCR type which had practically the same dimensions and arrangement throughout, for the responsible engineer, D. E. Marsh, had been Doncaster works manager before going to Brighton. The GWR 4-6-2 *Great Bear* of 1908 had a wide box with Belpaire top, a combination not repeated until the LMS Stanier Pacifics in 1933. Churchward put four $3\frac{3}{8}$in steel arch tubes into *Great Bear*'s firebox, the first application in Britain. After the last six LBSCR Atlantics of 1911 no further wide boxes were installed until the two Gresley Pacifics on the GNR in 1922, for the ability of the wide box to burn poorer coals was of little moment when first class steam coal was under £1 a ton.

Group railway requirements from 1923 led eventually to a revolution in boiler size and proportions. The increased lengths of through runs on the new LMS and LNER systems, and the heavier train weights and higher speeds developed on all four Groups required a substantial advance in locomotive power, and the two GNR Pacifics were the precursors. Coal consumptions and firing rates acceptable in 1914 could not be tolerated; Precursors and Experiments on 350-ton LNWR trains had then been fired at the rate of 100 to 130lb/sfg/hr and had consumed 55 to 60lb/mile. But the prime question was not efficiency but simply sheer evaporative power, and from the mid-1920s this was helped by a permitted increase in maximum axle load to 22 tons as a result of the Bridge Stress Committee's findings.

To meet the ever-rising requirements even within the relaxed weight limitations, scientific studies of locomotive boilers were made for the first time in Britain, and proportions were based largely on American test-plant data as analysed by Lawford Fry.[42] Particular aspects were the quantitive evaluation of the loss by unburned fuel at different firing rates, the importance of firebox volume with semi-bituminous coals, and the influence on evaporation of adequate free area through the tubes.

These considerations led to bigger boilers on existing wheel arrangements, which could be done on the permitted higher axle loads, and to the appreciation of the need for larger fireboxes to get more highly-rated radiant heating surface. In the immediate pre-Grouping times the firebox was producing about 30 per cent of the total evaporation. Only by the adoption of all these means could the necessary steam generation be attained, and augmented to keep pace with the steady increase in outputs through the 1930s.

In narrow-firebox 4-6-0s such as the Lord

Nelsons and Royal Scots some increase in firebox volume came from the bigger barrel diameter and from the extension of the throatplate forward by 9in or 10in to the barrel, an inversion of that curious try-out by Ivatt on one Stirling 8-footer by sloping the throatplate forward at the bottom to get a bigger nominal grate area. Hitherto inside fireboxes had rarely exceeded 8ft 6in in length; now they rose to 9ft 6in (Royal Scot) and 9ft 9in (Lord Nelson). Until Gresley's 1000-class Mogul of 1920 no parallel British boiler had reached 6ft diameter, and only *Great Bear* (1908) and the revised (1921) version of the GWR 4700-class 2-8-0 reached that dimension at the back of a taper barrel.

Otherwise maximum diameters had not exceeded 5ft 6in, but in the 1920s advanced to 5ft 9in. At the same time working pressures went up from the general non-GWR maximum of 200psi to 220-250psi. The biggest narrow-box pre-Group boilers, such as the 180psi 5ft 6in Atlantic type with a 9ft outside firebox and weighing 19 to 20 tons dry gave place to the 26-ton boilers such as those of the Nelsons and Scots, in which the previous high

firebox volume of 180-185cu ft gained by great depth was enhanced by the greater length and the larger barrel diameter.

A combustion chamber only a few inches long, plus a forward-sloping throatplate, was a feature of the 180psi GNR/LNER Pacifics of 1922-5, and was adopted to get a greater firebox heating surface and volume though a contributory reason in the first design was to reduce tube length below the useless 23ft of *Great Bear*. The A4 streamliners of 1935 had a combustion chamber 12in longer; firebox volume went up 17 per cent compared with the earlier Pacifics and firebox heating surface by 8 per cent for the same grate area. Biggest British fireboxes apart from those of the LNER and LMS Beyer-Garratt engines were in the LMS Coronation/Duchess (1938) and SR Merchant Navy (1941) 4-6-2s, and LNER class P2 Mikados (1934) at 275 to 300cu ft. In narrow boxes as retained for 4-4-0 and 4-6-0 locomotives no need arose for the forward-sloping throatplate to be extended into a combustion chamber.

With the general increase in Group express locomotive size the use of the taper boiler, hitherto almost confined to the GWR except for the 4in taper on the LSWR Urie 4-6-0s, spread to nearly all 10-wheelers and was universal in Pacifics except for the NER five of 1922-3. General views on this con-

Fig 15
LMS taper boiler for 2-6-4T engines, showing steam collector positioned above firebox tubeplate in endeavour to reduce water carry-over

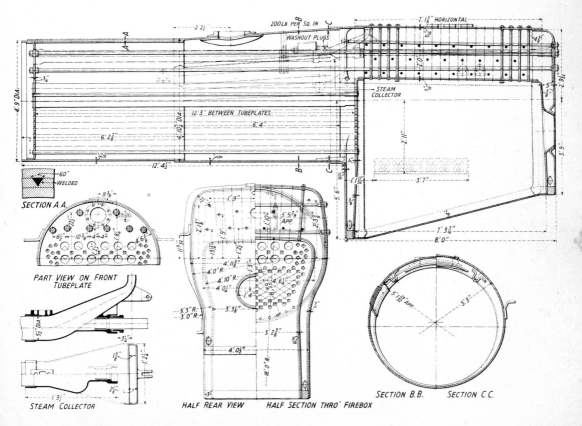

structural method have often been loose, with a vague statement of getting greater capacity at the back end. Actually the back end diameter was necessary in any case to get the needed free gas area through the tubes and flues to line up with the firebox proportions.

Taper down to the front enabled weight to be saved in the portion where evaporation was small and where a large water area was not so important. The actual shape and location of the taper had a decided effect on the full weight because of the different contained water capacities. GWR taper was along the top. SR taper was on the bottom, but sometimes in the front ring and sometimes in the back ring; LNER taper was on top and bottom, and on the LMS either on top or on both top and bottom.

An equally important factor leading to taper boilers was the need to give the driver ample visibility through the front windows of the cab, particularly in long 4-6-0, 2-6-2 and 4-6-2 engines. This was more important than could be appreciated by those unaccustomed to footplate travel; even with taper boilers the thick toughened-glass 4in side screens fitted from 1931 to many cabs were a decided help.

Despite the taper and permissible axle loads above 21 tons, the LMS Duchess boilers were so large (6ft 5½in max dia, 20ft 3in barrel length and 250lb pressure) that nickel steel had to be used to get within 22½ tons axle load, as it had in the last LNER Pacifics. For the same reasons Bulleid adopted a steel inside firebox with welded joints for the Merchant Navy Pacifics, and probably saved two tons in boiler weight compared with a rivetted copper inside box. At the rate to which the Merchant Navy boiler was forced on BR road tests, well over 40,000lb/hr evaporation, a copper box

probably would have given immense trouble by burning at the overlaps and leakage at tube ends.

In the final steam locomotive development under BR only one engine, *Duke of Gloucester*, needed the largest size of boiler, and the problems were more those of maintenance and operation. Careful thought was given to boiler design, and in none of the standard classes was the boiler the factor leading to shopping. Yet the Britannia Pacifics and other classes showed that a problem as old as the Stephenson-type locomotive had not been solved by the end, and that was water carry-over. High domes above large barrels were impossible; steam intake was scarcely 12in above working water level, and substantial water carry-over was prevalent in the Britannias until a slightly higher steam intake with a perforated water baffle below was installed.

Maximum service evaporation rates per unit of water level area increased three or four times between *Rocket* and the BR era – from 68 to 240-260lb/hr/sq ft of water level. Such rates usually were characterised by noticeable water carry-over, though not to the extent found in North America, or the extent found when British types were forced to their maximum on Rugby test plant, but enough to ensure no more than moderate final steam temperature, for the superheater had to act first as an evaporator. The low final steam temperatures were due also to grates and fireboxes being more than ample for the work normally extracted from them.

Boiler efficiencies in the last period of British steam often dropped as firing rates were increased, due mainly to more fuel going out the chimney unburned. Between Crewe and Carlisle LMS Royal Scots and Pacifics averaged only 6 or 7 per cent loss from this cause, but up the four miles of 1 in 75 to Shap summit the loss was 30 per cent, so that 4cwt of unburned cinders could be distributed over the track and surroundings with 400/500-ton trains.

Fig 16
Extended smokebox and double Kylchap exhaust of LNER three-cylinder 2-8-2 *Cock o' the North*, 1934. Smoke-deflecting shroud; whistle in front of chimney

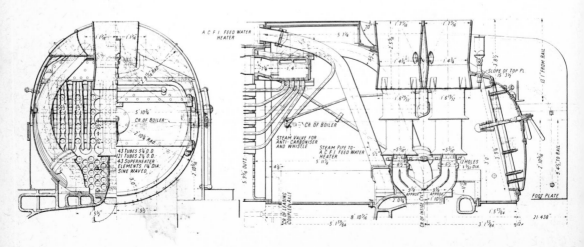

In capacity and layout a smokebox had to do with combustion and more particularly the after effects; its exhaust arrangements had a vital effect on the rate of steam generation. Thus the smokebox and its contents formed a sensitive part of the whole machine, the efficiency of which could be wrecked by an inch error in a vital dimension, or a fraction of an inch out of square for the blast pipe, or by a minute fraction of an inch air leakage round the smokebox door.

Earliest smokeboxes, made up of many plates, were carried down under the cylinders so that hot gas could circulate round the latter, but development soon led to the built-up horseshoe shape, with a separate bottom plate or covering above the cylinders and a rigid connection of the tubeplate to a frame stretcher or inside-cylinder block. The whole box became much sounder when outside cylinders were no longer attached to it, though that nefarious practice lasted until 1845-50 in the Hackworth sphere of influence. With the adoption of coal as fuel, increased smokebox capacity became desirable, but there was strange reluctance to provide this, and the smokebox congestion of many hard-worked engines led to incredible front-end conditions. With odd exceptions not until the installation of superheaters did extended smokeboxes become general.

Constructionally the greatest advance in smokebox construction was the belated adoption of the drumhead or circular smokebox tubeplate inserted in the front end of the barrel. This in itself reduced air leaks at the rear, but the further combination of this with a saddle support of the whole box improved front-end construction and airtightness substantially. Yet general adoption of this last feature was slow, and up to World War I years most large engines such as the LNWR Claughtons, Caledonian and GER 4-6-0s retained the horseshoe form, as did the much later LMS Royal Scots, and their smokebox troubles were widespread.

After the introduction of expansion valve motions in 1840-2 the only major advance in the basics of the reciprocating steam locomotive was high-temperature superheating. Spasmodic efforts were made in Britain from 1899 to 1915 with low-temperature smokebox superheaters such as the Aspinall and Phoenix, but they were too heavy and cumbersome for the mediocre results they brought. Practical means of attaining high superheat did not come until 1898-1900 through the work of Wilhelm Schmidt in Germany, and the first application in England was in May 1906 to GWR two-cylinder 4-6-0 No 2901 *Lady Superior* with a 24-element layout of 307sq ft of surface, followed in November-December the same year by two 0-6-0s Nos 898 and 900 on the LYR.

As in so many aspects of steam locomotive practice the idea far antedated the means of carrying it out. As far back as 1839 Hawthorn made a primitive trial on a locomotive for the eight-mile Newcastle & North Shields Railway, and McConnell had experimented on a small scale on the Southern Division of the LNWR in 1852-3. An editorial in *The Engineer* of 8 July 1859 remarked how wonderfully superheating quickened the flow of steam, and then went on to foreshadow the long-travel long-lap superheated locomotives of the 1930s: 'When we can introduce dry high-pressure steam protected from condensation and worked at a high rate of expansion we shall have compassed the most essential condition of locomotive improvement.' The only service application of superheating before the work of Schmidt and Aspinall in 1898-1900 was that of Martin's low-temperature apparatus with cylindrical headers in the smokebox which operated in at least 30 engines on the Grand Trunk Western in Canada around 1862.

Direct advantages of high superheat were the virtual elimination of condensation in the cylinders, even with early cut-offs, and the fact that at any given pressure each pound of steam occupied a greater volume according to the degree of superheat; but the complete lack of 'wetness' meant such steam had no emollient properties. This and the high temperature made lubrication the most difficult problem in the early years of superheating, and was the main cause of Churchward and his assistants devising the Swindon medium-temperature superheater with triple single-pass small-bore elements in each flue, whereby the standard sight-feed lubricator in the cab could be retained. The first of these was put into *Great Bear* in February 1908.

In 1910 only the GWR (29 engines) and LYR (27) had made any real use of high-temperature superheaters, and the only other railways trying them were the Caledonian (5), the Furness (5), and the GCR (1). But with a normal additon of 200 to 250°F to the saturated steam temperature, and with the usual short-lap short-travel valves of the time, the economies around 20-25 per cent in coal and water consumption on main-line duties could not be neglected, and applications were intensified.

By the beginning of World War I in August 1914 over 1500 engines were equipped and another 325 equipments were on order. After the GWR (801 engines) the greatest user was the LNWR (158) thanks to Bowen Cooke's adoption of Schmidt apparatus on the George V 4-4-0s and Prince of Wales 4-6-0s. By that time the GCR had 142 installations mainly of Robinson-Schmidt form, one of which was to a three-cylinder compound Atlantic.

From 1920 all new construction of main-line passenger and freight engines had superheaters, and such equipment was applied also to suburban tanks. Only the smaller type of shunter such as the NER class E1 0-6-0T, and Midland/LMS 'Jinty' 0-6-0Ts continued in new construction with saturated steam. Just as the quickening times, longer runs and increased train loads of the 1850s and 1860s could not have been maintained without expansion valve motions, so the Group railway demands on locomotive power could not have been met without superheating, and relative economy passed away as a talking point. Only superheating detail developments remained.

Of these the first to be solved, in pre-Group days, was that of cylinder diameter and boiler pressure. At first all superintendents except Churchward increased the cylinder size and lowered the boiler pressure with the idea of keeping the same tractive effort and reducing boiler maintenance charges. High boiler pressure (225psi), however, was an essential part of Churchward's programme and he provided valves and valve motions to suit it, whereas on other railways boiler pressure was advanced in niggardly stages of 5 and 10psi above 180psi when higher 'statutory' tractive effort and power could be obtained in no other way.

Traffic demands soon showed the pressure reduction to be unnecessary and impracticable. Moreover, the gradual disposal of lubrication difficulties made higher degrees of superheat acceptable, and the 18- to 24-element installations of 1906-14 progressed to 32- and 43-elements (LNER) and to 40 elements (LMS and SR). In theory the number and proportions of the elements should have depended on the duty, the planned normal rate of firing, and firebox volume, grate area, tube dimensions, and final steam temperature; but for generally equivalent duties British Pacific locomotives varied from 525 to 979sq ft of superheating surface, large-wheeled 4-6-0s from 295 to 490sq ft, and 0-6-0s from 185 to 275 sq ft.

On the GWR the small-bore (1in) triple single-pass elements and low temperature continued and the 14 elements and 262sq ft of the Stars and Courts were retained for the Castles and were increased only to 16 elements and 313sq ft in the Kings. Not until the last independent years of the GWR did high-temperature superheat and mechanical lubricators get on the Castles (380sq ft), and from 1953 under BR such equipment became standard for Castles and, at 489sq ft, for Kings, and helped performance to be maintained through deteriorating fuel and operating conditions.

Superheat attained in daily work was never high in Britain. On Anglo-Scottish runs final steam temperature with 225-250psi boiler pressure rarely reached 325°C (620°F), and the average throughout a run was usually only 275°C (550°F), whereas on the Continent values of 380°C (715°F) for steam pressures of 225-290psi were not uncommon when working hard.

Though 'Coke to Coal' is the title of this chapter some mention must be made of the use of oil fuel in Britain, though only the 20-year use of tar and other oils on the GER from 1888 was on the basis of economics. Apart from brief trials on odd engines on several railways 1898-1903 the other applications of oil-burning in Britain were purely temporary in conception, due to coal strikes (1912) and to coal shortages arising mainly from politico-economic circumstances (1920-1 and 1948). In no cases did operation continue long enough for success to be ensured; and the several years of trials with pulverised coal and colloidal fuel in three GCR 2-8-0s over 1920-3 met insoluble practical problems.

Financial economy in the GER scheme was almost nil because the oil averaged £1.40/ton compared with half that price for coal. The main reason for the long use was to consume a by-product otherwise difficult of disposal; and when more and more train lights were turned over to electricity there was no economy at all in buying high-grade oil outside, and so the system lapsed, after up to 80 engines at a time had been fitted at a cost of £50-60 an engine.

# 8　From Iron to Steel

Working of iron was still by primitive means for the various parts of a locomotive through the decade when George Stephenson was holding the fort alone, and for years thereafter. Eventually manufacture and machining of wrought, rolled and cast irons were brought near perfection, but by then the production of steel had become technically and commerically sound, and the gradual change from iron to steel as the basic material transformed the structure of the locomotive and permitted the increase in size and power required by the growing industrialisation of the country.

Increased tensile and shearing strengths were the main reasons for the change to steel, enabling greater loads to be taken through the same scantlings, and permitting increase in size and power without proportionate thickening of the material. Where ductility or wearing qualities were needed, iron was given up slowly, and Low Moor iron boilers, wrought iron wheel centres and cast iron axleboxes and guides continued to be made until the 1890s. Rolled steel for most purposes was higher in first cost than iron until a decided cheapening through 1881-5. Cast steel was always higher in price per ton than cast iron, but its greater strength and resistance in all aspects except wear, permitted economic replacement of complex iron and steel forgings where the number off was sufficient to cover the cost of patterns.

Cogitation on the hand-made taps and dies used by George Stephenson at Killingworth, displayed at York, will give some idea of what many early locomotive constructors had to contend with, remembering that for an appreciable part of annual working hours such tools were used by candle light and dim natural light. Stephenson probably made those taps himself; they were not of Maudslay's triple-pass type that later became standard.

Though better facilties were denied Stephenson, concurrently Henry Maudslay was approaching the zenith of his powers at his new Lambeth factory. With him began the science of precise engineering measurement and the use of metals and machines that could repeat the precisions. He developed the first accurate plane surfaces for machine tools, the first accurate lathes with iron beds, and the first precision power-driven screw-cutting lathes with slide rests and in which threads of any pitch could be cut by a combination of gear wheels and a changeable lead screw.

He evolved standard nuts and bolts for use in his own factory, made the first iron floor cranes, and trained up in high-quality production a succession of leading engineers, two of whom directly (Richard Roberts and James Nasmyth) and one indirectly (Joseph Whitworth) profoundly influenced locomotive manufacture. The Maudslay works remained in business with a high reputation until 1899, and in them was trained Collett, the penultimate chief mechanical engineer of the GWR, who made notable advances in Swindon shop practice and equipment.

Machine tools of the quality and accuracy of Maudslay's did not spread widely through industry as it then was, but after 1836 methods in locomotive factories developed to suit the increasing demand. In the late 1830s skilled and forward engineers such as Richard Roberts and Daniel Gooch were using templates to ensure the same leading dimensions through a batch of hand-made locomotives, in Gooch's case for engines built at several widely-separated works. More accurate manufacture was helped by the limited adoption of gauges for the measurement of certain details. Roberts introduced this in 1825 for textile machinery and used it to some extent in locomotives before 1840 and more widely thereafter. McConnell of the Southern Division of the LNWR recorded in the late 1840s that a few years before he had received from Sharp Roberts a spare cylinder that needed no fitting up and went into its place exactly, and spoke of this as altogether exceptional.

General closer tolerances and more accurate measurement and machining as a matter of daily practice on a wide scale could not come until Joseph Whitworth's introduction of 'master' plane surfaces, 'go and not go' gauges, and standard sizes and threads for nuts and bolts, the germ for all of which he had gathered in his time at Maudslay's works, where small 'plane tables' were used for workers to test the smoothness of their work. Before 1848-50 every bolt was made up as an individual piece from a rough bar or forging, and innumerable thread pitches and forms existed. Many bolts, and even other small forgings, were made up to sketches prepared by the erecting charge-hand when he found just what he needed for the work in hand.

Growing availability of rolled iron plates up to the maximum needed for locomotives from around 1855-60 brought possibilities of considerable improvement in locomotive construction. Inside and outside frame plates hitherto had been built up of sections forge-welded together, and either cut by hand or trimmed up and surfaced by hand after simple drilling and slotting of part of the profile. Big advances in machine tools were made through the

1850s, but no planing machine could deal at one pass with the flat top edge of a locomotive frame 20ft or more in length. Items such as cylinder flanges and faces and motion plates were only partly machined, and 'shaping' was still by hand chisel, file and scraper, and individually fitted by the same tools, though frame slotters were in use from the 1840s.

These manufacturing methods, the crude shops, primitive lighting, and under-developed power supplies and drives enforced the adjustable bearings and other details that were universal. Wedge and gib-and-cotter adjustments for big and small ends and for coupling rod ends enabled service wear in the brasses to be taken up, but their primary purpose was to cover inaccuracies in machining and first erection. Not uncommon works records of those times could read 1/16in or $\frac{1}{8}$in short in distance between driving and trailing wheels, $\frac{3}{8}$in long between driving and front wheels, and 1/16in or more out of square between one side and the other. Shop drawings of connecting and coupling rods often gave no centre-to-centre length, this being adjusted by the forge-men to the requirements of the charge-hand erector. One of the first things Ramsbottom had to do on taking charge of Crewe works in August 1857 was to have added to each drawing a note 'Work to dimensions'.

Richard Roberts devised a simple planer in 1817 for small general work, but a big step forward did not come until 1842 when Whitworth began production of his reversible-toolbox planer that could cut in each direction. Gradually these and rugged shapers (developed much by Nasmyth), slotters, drills and screw-cutting lathes of greater range and accuracy found their way into locomotive shops, and though they did not approach the thousandth of an inch standards of modern times, or even the one sixty-fourth of the 1920s, they served their purpose. Indeed, they sometimes served more than their purpose; simple and robust shapers and slotters bought in 1847 were still in use at Crewe works at the time of the 1923 Grouping. They were samples of an obsolescence that enforced the complete reorganisation and re-equipment of that plant over the years 1924-28 by the new owner, the LMS.

Principal practical defect of the steam locomotive was that by the whole nature of the reciprocating direct drive, and the way the chassis developed, it became the most effective wear-producer known, engendering friction in a hundred flat and cylindrical metal-to-metal surfaces throughout the length and breadth of engine and tender, moving over each other all the time, and some of them subject to no lubrication from one year's end to another. Added to this friction were constant shocks from the reciprocating drive and from the movement over the track. In the driving mechanism alone, for example, a GNR Atlantic on a journey from London to York experienced 95,000 reversals of stress, plus 25,000 separate uncushioned shocks on each wheel-and-axle pair through rail joints and points which had to be taken up by springs to prevent transfer *in toto* to the rest of the machine.

All this required constant maintenance and periodic heavy repair and renewal, involving high wages costs, great capital investment, and substantial continuous expenditure on spares, machine tools and plant. Yet directors were generally reluctant to sanction expenditure, particularly of new capital, on machinery or works extensions.

From the time of the SDR railways established their own works for locomotive major repairs, but with growth in mileage, traffic and engine stock the original works could not always be extended. As early as 1840 the GJR had to consider moving its works from Edge Hill, Liverpool, to a more commodious site, and at this juncture Joseph Locke, as chief engineer, proposed that future locomotives should be built at the new factory. This was largely because Locke was being forced to the idea of a new standard locomotive to replace the troublesome Patentees from several makers with which the GJR had been worked since 1837. The result was Crewe works, which completed its first new locomotive in 1843.

Other railways gradually followed suit in one degree or another. Opposition could not be raised by private builders at that time because the quite undeveloped industry was rarely keeping pace in design or in quality of construction, though certain builders such as Stephenson and Sharp Roberts influenced general design from the outset. In 1850 Locke gave[43] the construction cost of locomotives built at Crewe as less by the 20 per cent profit he presumed was made by private builders. Robert Stephenson at once refuted this by saying that on the last £240,000 worth of machinery built at the Newcastle factory there had been a loss of £1,200, and he quoted figures from the LMR to show that the claimed cheaper cost of railway-built locomotives, said to be £400 less than bought-in locomotives, did not include all materials, or any allowance for coal, power, capital, rent, rates or taxes.

This remained a contentious point to the end of steam. Naturally financial overheads per new locomotive would tend to be smaller in a works whose main business was the steady overhaul of 10 to 20 times the number of new locomotives built than they could be in a factory devoted to new construction with a fluctuating demand, and one in which locomotive building was the sole or main source of profit instead of a working expense.

Midland Kirtley outside-frame 2-4-0 of the 1860s, as No 158A in the MR duplicate list. Some of these engines lasted into LMSR days and this one has been preserved.

Following in the wake of the great Maudslay-trained engineers a generation of locomotive works engineers arose in the 1850s that revolutionised the standards and equipment of manufacture and materials. Prominent were Charles Beyer, Henry Dubs and John Ramsbottom, each of whom had spent a time when young at the Manchester works of Sharp Roberts and must have been influenced directly by the mechanical genius of Richard Roberts.

In later years Beyer (1854-5) and Dubs (1863) were able to plan and erect complete locomotive-building plants of their own in which maximum use was made of the latest machine tools, gauges and templates, and in which provision was made for subsequent works extensions as part of a planned whole and without upsetting the nucleus or the work flow.

Beyer, as chief engineer of Sharp Bros, had appreciated Whitworth's standardising and measuring work, and from the beginning Gorton Foundry production was based on true plane surfaces, standard threads, plug gauges, and the use of the so-called graduating machine, which in essence was a screw-cutting lathe with precision-made lead screw

and a measuring attachment on the slide rest to mark pieces for machining, and to make other measuring items, such as patternmakers' rules, for distribution through the shops. Beyer, who had a name for elegance in design, believed in robust construction before appearance in order to maintain for as long as possible in service the accurate centre lines and squareness he had taken some trouble to achieve, and from Gorton Foundry beginnings he used 1in main frames whenever he could on six-wheelers of 20 to 30 tons, and some of which lasted from 1860 to 1920.

Ramsbottom's main task from 1857 was the complete reorganisation of Crewe works from a factory with 'hand-made' productions in which startling departures from marked dimensions were permitted, to a works whose products were based on accurately made standardised components and capable of handling about 1000 heavy repairs a year contrasted with 400 14 years earlier. Ramsbottom was an unusual combination of good organiser, competent administrator, and practical engineer. From the 1850s there was wide acceptance of his inventions of the split piston ring, safety valve, double-beat regulator, screw reverse, cylinder lubricator, feed pump regulation, and, after his death, of the water pick-up he had invented and applied on the LNWR in 1860. At Longsight and Crewe from 1842 to

1871 he was constantly devising new machines and processes to do work more accurately and cheaply.

Matthew Kirtley, locomotive superintendent of the Midland from 1847 to 1873, was an engineer to whom little credit has been given for his works practice and administration. As a designer he was noted for robustness, rather than for innovation, though from 1862-3 he combined both in 0-6-0s with frames slotted from rectangular rolled plates that gave greater support round the horns. He had final responsibility for the brick arch and firehole deflector development outlined in Chapter 7; he pushed the development of welded iron boilers into the strongest of the time in the late 1850s and 1860s; and under him was initiated at Derby works over the years 1858-63 what was probably the first attempt at a limits-and-fits system of gauging in a railway-owned works.

This last-named activity was based primarily on Whitworth's practice and the development of his plane surface into a marking-off table for details and a more accurate procedure in setting up frames in the erecting shop. Precision (for the time) moulding was also introduced in the foundry, particularly for cylinder castings, this at a time when high quality, toughness and wearing properties of cast iron were being achieved. By 1855-8 the shrinkage in iron castings was only half what it had been 15 to 20 years earlier. This helped precision,

North Eastern long-boiler 0-6-0 of the early 1860s. Sandwich frame flitching plates still with rivetted horn plates; dome 35 per cent of boiler diameter.

and also changed the patternmakers' and moulders' arts; and to historians it also illuminates some of the difficulties of the early builders in getting sound cylinders and locomotives.

From the 1820s rolled iron plates around $\frac{3}{8}$in thick suitable for locomotive boilers could be obtained from Longridge's Bedlington Ironworks, but until the mid-1830s they rarely exceeded 4ft square; by 1837-8 4ft plates of 7ft to 8ft length were available. A Planet locomotive with a boiler barrel 3ft dia by 5ft long and a 4ft by 2ft 6in outer firebox required 22 plates, which was not much improvement over the 28 to 36 plates in the Wylam locomotives 15 years before. Joints throughout were of the lap type, and every one was liable to leak for neither the accuracy of surface nor the skill in hand rivetting, lapping and caulking was high. The butt strap and joint were later developments, and in locomotive work seem to have come first at the works of Sharp Bros around 1847.

Available plate sizes grew slowly, and for years the larger sizes were adopted reluctantly because homogenity could not be guaranteed, particularly when thickness got above $\frac{3}{8}$in. Even in 1847 the firebox wrapper of the broad-gauge *Iron Duke*, then the largest locomotive boiler in the kingdom, was made up of five separate lap-jointed plates. By that time Yorkshire iron had gained its reputation for boiler plates, largely because William Fairbairn's tests of 1838 showed it to have an ultimate tensile strength some 10 per cent above the Derbyshire, Staffordshire and Shropshire brands, and with superior homogenity.

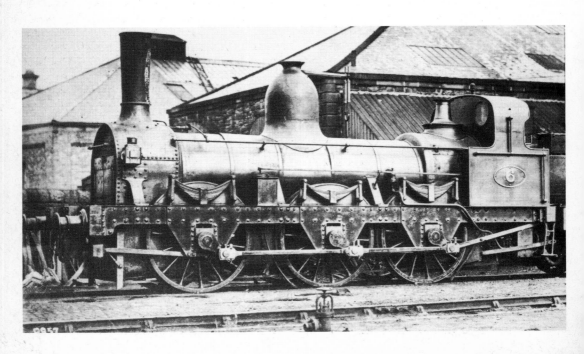

Early domes were small in size, being limited by boiler plate dimensions. The huge domes of the 1840s and 1850s were practicable structurally only when a barrel ring could be obtained in one plate. Those great domes helped the dry pipe to function more in accordance with its name, but were a source of weakness as the diameter of some was 35 per cent of the barrel diameter. No early solution was found to the method of water-sealing the firebox at the bottom or at the firehole.

Hand rivetting was universal until the 1860s and the results given by early power rivetters were not always superior in tightness or speed of work. Rivet holes were punched, not drilled, through the plates until the 1870s, and even then punching was often preferred for iron boilers as giving slightly conical holes that were better filled by the hot hand-driven rivets. Punching and shearing machines came into use in the 1840s, but only with steel boilers did drilling of rivet holes become general. Power flanging over blocks was unknown until the mid-1850s; before that square corners joined by angle irons were not uncommon for outer fireboxes.

Because of low barrel pitch quite a number of boilers from 1835 to 1855 were made two or three inches oval with the shorter axis across the barrel, in order to get in the maximum number of tubes, and had a row of stays across the minor axis.

The amount of handwork needed for quarter of a century on barrel and firebox plates well warranted the term boilersmiths. It also helped to limit boiler pressures, and the 120psi adopted for the Jenny Linds in 1847 needed exceptional care in boiler making. A dozen years later pressure still normally did not exceed 120lb, but by then boiler manufacture was more accurate and under greater control, and double-rivetted butt straps were in more general use for longitudinal seams. Pressures above 150psi could scarcely be used until double-strap butt joints, steel plates and drilled holes came into vogue.

Longitudinal lap seams were always a source of weakness as long cracks tended to develop close to them where the shape departed from the truly circular and two plate thicknesses became one. This started the path to many of the boiler explosions that occurred until the mid-1880s though the final cause was usually the lack of inspection of the boiler interior. The go-as-you-please policy of the time, which in locomotive departments reached its peak on the NER under Edward Fletcher, gave that company 10 out of the 16 locomotive boiler explosions recorded over the years 1875-80. Board of Trade enquiries often showed a complete lack of internal inspection. The many fewer boiler explosions of the 20th Century were nearly always due to running with low water, resulting in a collapsed firebox crown rather than a rupture of the shell, though a notable exception was the 1922 Buxton explosion of an LNWR 0-8-0 due to safety-valve binding.

In the late 1850s the Midland developed forge-welded boiler rings, with each ring united to the next by a 10in wide shrunk-on external hoop double rivetted, and with the front of the first ring thickened for flanging outwards to take a flat tubeplate. By 1866 there were 19 such boilers at work in which the centre shrunk-on ring also formed the dome base. Manufacturing cost was said to be £465 against the £415 for the structure of a normal lap-rivetted boiler 4ft dia by 11ft barrel length.[44] The system was to be adopted permanently, but seems to have died out with the change in superintendents in 1873.

In 1859 *The Engineer* stressed: 'Steel in locomotive construction must largely replace iron,' and in that year odd applications to boiler shells were made on the GNR and in 1862-3 on the GWR. By 1862 Krupp was prepared to roll steel plates in widths up to 15ft, which made possible single-ring barrels, but many years elapsed before that feature was established, first in Gresley's 2-6-0 No 1000 on the GNR in 1920. Possession of a Bessemer steel rolling mill from 1866, plus Webb's experience in the steel industry 1866-70, led the LNWR to pioneer the consistent manufacture of steel boilers from 1872, but Webb was then following a policy initiated by his predecessor, Ramsbottom, and his suggestion of all future boilers in steel put to the directors in January 1872 was based specifically on the condition of a prototype steel boiler built in 1865.

Several Planet and Bury engines on the LMR had iron inside fireboxes, as had the American Norris engines on the Birmingham & Gloucester 1839-42, and there were always a few locomotives running about with iron inside boxes until the 1870s. Steel fireboxes were tried on the Maryport & Carlisle and Scottish Central in 1862-4 and on the Caledonian in 1870-1, all these being good water lines, and on the North London in 1873-7, but only the two first named had any success. The NLR boxes had to be withdrawn after less than 100,000 miles.

Despite the efforts of Webb on the LNWR steel never caught on in Britain for inside fireboxes until Bulleid began to apply them on the SR in 1941, though there was the mass application to the Railway Operating Division (ROD) 2-8-0s in 1917-19, but when those engines came back on to British railways many of the steel boxes were replaced by copper.

Reluctance to use steel fireboxes was not because British steel was inferior. Many boxes of English and Scottish plates were put into export orders and gave satisfaction; but no persevering attempt was made on a British railway despite the potential saving in weight and cost, partly, in this century, because with large locomotives working under high load factor and watered at widely separated points, water softening was needed. In his experiments Webb set out to do more than get a steel box; he sought to eliminate side stays and reduce others, and to prevent super rigidity that might bring cracks. He also put in water bottoms, combustion chambers and other novelties, and so in the end he achieved unsatisfactory results in 1888-90 with both his square corrugated box and his figure-8 shape.

The thin-spoked one-piece cast iron wheels of the Killingworth and early SDR engines were almost the weakest part of the locomotive, partly because the crankpin was attached crudely to one of the spokes and breakages were incessant. The cast iron two-piece plug wheels used on the SDR from 1826-7 (see Chapter 3) even by 1845 had practical applications limited to a top speed of 15mph in combination with a maximum axle load of 8 to 10 tons. Tyre developments on these and other early wheels have been mentioned in Chapter 3. The first separate tyres at Killingworth and Hetton, and probably the first few of those on the SDR, were hand forged and had variations in thickness and from the true circular shape, but by 1830 Bedlington had begun to roll flanged tyres, though of course the final weld had still to be made before shrinkage on the rim.

Richard Roberts patented in 1832 a wheel with wrought iron spokes having T-heads at the outer ends rivetted to wrought iron rims, but the Sharp Roberts engines for the Dublin & Kingstown in 1834-5 had cast iron wheels with the same spoke section. Bury's early 2-2-0s and 0-4-0s generally had wheels akin to those of the Roberts 1832 patent. Robert Stephenson's 1833 patent[45] for cast iron naves and wrought iron rims connected by malleable iron gas pipes set at alternate slopes was the last, and not very successful, endeavour before acceptance of wrought iron spokes and rims as the only method giving sufficient strength and reliability. Occasional fully wrought wheels were known from 1836-7, but until around 1850 with a few exceptions the cast iron hub was retained and various methods adopted for the connection to it of wrought iron spokes.

Through the late 1830s and 1840s forging of wheel centres was entirely by hand. One spoke was forged to one curved rim section and each end of the section forged to the next. At Sharp Roberts three or four spokes were forged to a flat rim section, and then these flat assemblies were forged into one and the whole bent hot round a cast iron centre former that had projections to determine the spoke position; finally an iron hub was cast round the inner ends of the spokes. Despite the labour and expense in forg-

ing this procedure was economic because the wheels of Sharpie 2-2-2s were standard over considerable numbers, and as they were for inside-cylinder single drivers they had not the complication of a crank arm. Some tender wheels of this Sharpie construction lasted on Hayling Island into this century, and the tyres were observed to be fastened by deeply countersunk bolts passing right through tyre and rim, a method used on occasion into the 1860s.

Spokes as a rule were either circular or rectangular in section, tending towards the latter. A few ECR 2-2-2s of 1844 had driving and carrying wheels in which the major axes of adjacent spokes were at right angles to each other. From 1844 to 1849 Stephenson long-boiler and other engines had spokes and rims formed of T-angles, two of which were set back to back to give a cruciform spoke section; by this means the cost of a full forging was obviated. Well over 1000 such wheels were made for English-built long-boiler engines. Many Hawthorn engines for slow-speed service from 1847 to 1851 had solid iron wheels, both coupled and carrying, as had some earlier machines by Shepherd & Todd. These were cheaper than forgings but had a limited range and were noisy.

Nasmyth's steam hammer, invented 1842, came into more general use from around 1850 and helped the whole wheel-making process, which then remained much the same until wrought wheels were replaced gradually by steel castings from 1884-6. From 1855-6 Beyer Peacock forged each spoke solid with a segment of the hub; the several sections were connected at the hub through keys of green iron driven into diamond-section keyways and this iron being more easily fused than the steel of the hub formed a sort of flux that helped the hammer welding.

Some of the finest specimens of wrought iron were the 7ft 9in centres of the Conner 8ft 2in 2-2-2s on the Caledonian and the 7ft 8in centres of the Stirling 8-footers. The former had 28 spokes and for the first time crescent balance weights were forged integral with the rim; the latter had 24 spokes and square-ended balance weights. Cast steel wheels were used for the Stirlings from 1887. This material was introduced first in 1884 on GER 2-4-2Ts for driving and coupled wheels and from the previous year in carrying wheels. Long before this, at the London exhibition of 1862, several crucible cast steel wheels were shown, including a wheel-and-crank-axle set by Naylor with 7ft corrugated disc centres, the corrugations being not primarily for transverse strength but to facilitate pouring. Stamped wheels, also, were introduced at that time by Owen of Rotherham, but they seem to have been confined to rolling stock.

Cast iron centres were used often for industrial

shunters and also in the late Victorian period for shunters and local mineral engines on the GWR, GER and one or two Scottish railways. Webb applied cast iron driving and coupled wheel centres with H-section spokes to about 1400 coal and shunting engines with 4ft 3½in tread diameter from 1872 to 1900 and they gave excellent service. The last great application of cast iron wheel centres was to the Austerity 0-6-0ST shunters of World War II, when cast steel was in short supply and the locomotives themselves were stipulated to be capable of four or five years of arduous work and then could go for scrap. In fact most of them were in service for a score of years without any wheel troubles, and a few more were built for the NCB in post-war years.

In November 1840 Daniel Gooch took out a patent for putting a steel wearing surface on iron tyres, and such tyres were used on GWR engines through Gooch's time at Swindon, and a grinding machine was devised to true the hard surface. From 1856 crucible cast steel tyres were in limited use on the NLR, ECR and LNWR largely through the sales efforts of Longsdon, the English representative of Krupp, and only the high cost retarded a much wider adoption.

The first Krupp set went on to one of the NLR four-coupled tanks in 1856; by May 1859 it had run 64,280 miles for a tread wear of 0.3in, said to be one-third the wear of a normal tyre but with a purchase price eight times greater. This wear rate was equalled on the ECR on which a set of Krupp tyres introduced in April 1857 showed no need for a re-turning after 80,000 miles. The NLR had another 12 engines equipped 1857-8 and when they had reached 44,000 miles no turning was needed,

Stirling eight-footer No 5, built at Doncaster 1873, heading a southbound train at York, probably in the 1890s. (K. H. Leech collection)

whereas a comparison set in Yorkshire iron had to be removed after 34,000 miles and two re-turnings. Several sets of Krupp tyres were fitted by the LNWR in 1858.

From 1860 crucible cast steel tyres became more general, but after the LNWR opened its Bessemer steel plant in 1866, rolled steel tyres replaced the crucible cast type and soon a thousand a year were being made at Crewe on a method evolved by Ramsbottom making use of powerful horizontal duplex steam hammers to get the ingot ready for the rolling mill.

The steam hammer in locomotive factories accelerated and consolidated the manufacture of such large constituents as axles and reversing shafts, and lighter hammers eased the rapid production of innumerable smaller items like intermediate valve spindles, eccentric rods, crankpins, brake hangers and drawhooks, and were of great utility when steel began to be used for such parts in the 1860s. In particular, the manufacture of wrought iron crank axles was improved and the reliability of the material enhanced because the cranks could be forged by bending and the fibre of the iron maintained through the axle uninterruptedly. From the 1830s forging had had to be done laboriously with three or four separate pieces forge-welded together to form half an axle, and then the two halves were lapped together over the centre section for the final forging into one piece.

Krupp steel axles came into limited use from 1859. The LNWR ordered a double-throw four-bearing axle for one of McConnell's big 18in outside-frame 2-2-2s of the 300-class in 1859 at a cost of £231 but only on the condition that the maker would replace it free on any defect or rupture except one due to a derailment. At the same time one axle of Lancashire steel and two from Sheffield were bought at a cheaper price. Sheffield forged

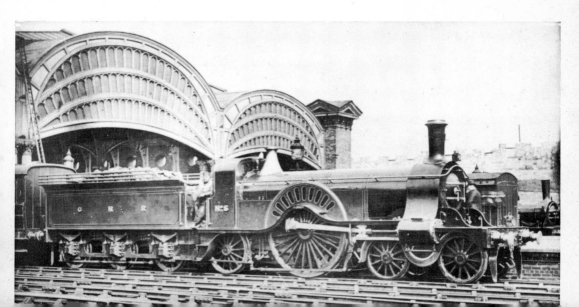

steel crank axles came first in 1866 with trials on two or three railways, but crank axles of that type did not supersede wrought iron for another 20 years or so except at Crewe.

Perfection of forging processes and improvement in steel increased the number of inside-cylinder locomotives in the late Victorian age until in 1897 there was scarcely a railway building outside-cylinder locomotives when only two cylinders were used; but with the larger engines constructed from 1899-1900 increasing cylinder diameters and piston thrusts caused a reversion to outside cylinders or the adoption of multi-cylinder propulsion, because when cylinders were increased above 19½in dia space could not be found for adequate axle and crankpin journals and web widths plus four eccentrics.

With the increasing stresses doubt also arose as to crank axle steel characteristics, some lines like the Midland favouring a 'soft' steel of low tensile strength and great ductility while others like the NER preferred harder steels of 38-40 tons/sq in ultimate strength. To get full advantage of the latter, and to ease the whole manufacture, built-up crank axles were introduced on some railways. They were made practicable by the higher standard of shop methods, and here again Webb was a pioneer for he introduced the first one in the late 1890s and is believed to have used a low nickel steel.

Large rolled iron plates transformed main frame design, strength and manufacture principally because numerous bolted and rivetted connections along the side plates could be eliminated and no working could occur between individual frame and horn plates. In this aspect the plate frame was ahead of the bar frame, for not until the casting of a whole side frame in one piece in the 20th Century could a main bolted joint at a highly stressed location be eliminated from bar frame construction.

By the 1860s single rolled iron plates to suit 2-4-0s and 0-6-0s were available though not in general use, but by then in the larger works the old type of sectional frame was being welded up under 10cwt steam hammers. Advantage was sometimes taken of the sectional method to enlarge the area round driving and coupled axleboxes to get the box central in the frames, and even, as in the Met tanks at a width of 5in, to act as the axlebox guide thrust face. In some designs this thickened section was used to change the distance between frames fore and aft of it to get an extra two or three inches firebox width or to suit cylinder spacing. By the time of these developments frame conditions themselves had eased through the elimination of the frame-firebox tie-in and the substitution of expansion brackets, so that despite greater locomotive size and power the frames from the 1860s were a far more rigid and better maintenance proposition than those of the 1840s and 1850s.

With the increase in size of rolled plates, progressive steps had to be made in machine tools that could handle them, but probably not until the Smith & Beecroft machine introduced 1858-9 was there a frame slotter of accuracy able to take more than one set of frame plates. For long years thereafter the method of frame contouring remained awkward. From the rectangular plate the contour was shaped roughly by punching or drilling overlapping holes round a template, annealing and straightening to remove any strains caused by punching, and then putting six to 10 plates together on a slotter for the final machining, after which the plater and his mate with large hammers gave a final straightening to individual plates laid on large cast iron slabs.

Steel plates without any thickening over iron permitted higher piston loads to be absorbed and greater weight supported, but in the 20th Century with larger 4-4-2, 4-6-0 and 4-6-2 locomotives the almost standard 1in was thickened whenever weight permitted to 1⅛in and even 1¼in; so small an addition as 1/16in was appreciated by some designers. Cross staying was the weak point, though alleviated by the use of steel castings for inside motion plates. Some of these castings, as on GCR 4-4-2, 4-6-0, 2-8-0 and 2-6-4T classes, were used to give great support at the location where the frame plates were set in at the front to clear the side movement of guiding wheels.

Only in the twilight of steam were horizontal or racking stays adopted to any extent. They were difficult to apply with inside cylinders or inside motion, and an advantage of outside-cylinders with outside valves and motion was always the possible stronger frame structure − if designers were so minded. They were not always so minded, because long decades of inside cylinders and motion and flabby frames brought designers to a self-defensive postulate that frames ought to be made deliberately with a little lateral flexibility. So frames became the weak point in large 20th Century multi-cylinder locomotives such as the GWR four-cylinder types and the LMS Royal Scots. By 1939 not one of the 79 Gresley 180lb and 220lb three-cylinder Pacifics of 1922-34 was still running with its original frames,[46] and rate of Royal Scot frame cracks had more than quadrupled in six years.

Not until the Bulleid Pacifics of 1941 did a designer show how ample horizontal bracing could be provided with an inside cylinder, crank throw and motion. The later BR two-cylinder 4-6-2s and 2-10-0s with clear space between the frames also had full racking stays. In all three classes just mentioned was revived the old Beyer-Met practice of the frame centred above the axleboxes; and the BR types also followed the practice evolved on the LMS of link-and-pin cross tie-rods between the frames at the horns, and manganese steel liners for boxes and horns that greatly reduced the wear.

Towards the end of steam the composition of the usual 26/30-ton mild steel for frames was adjusted to suit oxy-acetylene flame cutting, for that process reduced considerably the time taken in preparation and machining. Then steel suitable for welding was introduced with small quantities of copper, chromium and manganese, and ultimate strengths up to 35-40 tons/sq in. By this means many bolted and rivetted connections could be obviated and the whole frame structure made up as one piece, an idea foreshadowed in England in 1869 when Webb had proposed that 'the frames, cross stays and back carriages are cast in steel with the necessary hornblocks enclosed and fixed in one piece'. Undeveloped foundry and machining techniques at that time prevented practical application.

From 1920 alloy steels were used increasingly for driving parts partly to cope with rising piston thrusts but mainly to reduce the weight of reciprocating and revolving parts that had to be balanced by weights in the wheels, and to decrease hammer blow. Only the GWR retained carbon steel for these constituents, but by heat treatment increased the strength to 38-40 tons/sq in. This railway also kept to rectangular sections for coupling rods. Other Group lines used 3 per cent nickel steel and nickel-chrome-molybdenum steels up to 60-65 tons/sq in ultimate strength, and favoured pronounced I-sections for connecting and coupling rods, sometimes with webs only $\frac{3}{8}$in thick. To reduce weight and eliminate joints Gresley forged the piston and rod in one piece of nickel steel, a practice tried by Hackworth in 1849 and by McConnell in the 1850s with wrought iron.

Efforts to balance revolving weights are believed to have been made late in 1837 by Dawson, running foreman on the London & Southampton at Nine Elms with a panel between two spokes opposite the crank, and this was noted and adopted by Sharp Roberts in 1838 but with weights in the rims. In the latter year Heaton, who had been balancing stationary engines from 1810-12, made suggestions for balance weights in the wheels and some Bury four-wheelers on the London & Birmingham were so treated. Working independently, Hunt on the North Union in 1839-40 fitted weights to the driving wheels of Bury 2-2-0s primarily to try and ease pronounced fore-and-aft surging that was breaking intermediate drawbars. In 1844 Gray balanced the wheels of his large 0-6-0s on the Hull & Selby. From this time the practice of adding weights to the wheel rims or boss opposite the crank arm grew slowly.

The early efforts related only to revolving weights. The first man to suggest balance of reciprocating parts was J. G. Bodmer in a patent of 1834 for an opposed-piston engine, and in the 1840s two or three of his locomotives were tried on the London & Brighton and South Eastern railways but with an ingenious arrangement that brought the drive from both pistons out of the back end of the cylinders. First to make the compromise of balancing reciprocating parts by revolving weights in the wheels was J. Fernihough, ex-Bury locomotive superintendent of the Eastern Counties in 1844. He may have been led to this by a letter from T. R. Crampton to *The Railway Times* in 1843 drawing attention to the 'unbalance' arising from reciprocating parts but offering no suggestions. The practice of balancing reciprocating parts really extended only after the publication in 1855 of D. K. Clark's *Railway Machinery* in which he gave the rules and proportions to be observed.

Clark's recommendation that two-thirds of the reciprocating weights should be balanced in the wheels derived from his experience with 2-2-2s, 2-4-0s, 0-4-2s and 0-6-0s of 20 to 30 tons weight, but was largely perpetuated in Britain until after World War I, no more understanding of the compromise principle having been attained than in the case of slide valves and valve motions. The LMS class 5 4-6-0s with 6ft wheels and 66 per cent of the reciprocating weights balanced in the wheels showed a clear wheel lift of 2in at speed of 7.8 revs/sec, corresponding to 100mph, and of course the wheel came down with a corresponding blow.

Only the investigations of the Bridge Stress Committee in the early 1920s showed this proportion to be needlessly high in the large engines of the time and could be reduced without deleteriously affecting the riding and with benefit to the bridges, because at 5 revs/sec the hammer blow from driving wheels of some of the engines tested was 50 per cent more than the static axle load. An immediate result was that civil engineers raised from 20 to 22 tons the permissible axle load for carefully balanced multi-cylinder locomotives, but close attention had to be paid to low hammer blow per wheel, per axle, per rail and per engine.

To ease the wear on axleboxes and guides resulting from the different angles of drives and coupling rods on the two sides, Stroudley (LBSCR), Dean (GWR), Hill (GER) and others from time to time on inside-cylinder locomotives put the driving crank and coupling rod crank on each side at the same angle. This practice brought a bigger balance weight in the wheel but did not increase the hammer blow. It was followed as late as 1928 in the two-cylinder ex-GER type 4-6-0s built by Beyer Peacock for the LNER. Partial balance of inside-cylinder locomotives could be achieved by prolonging

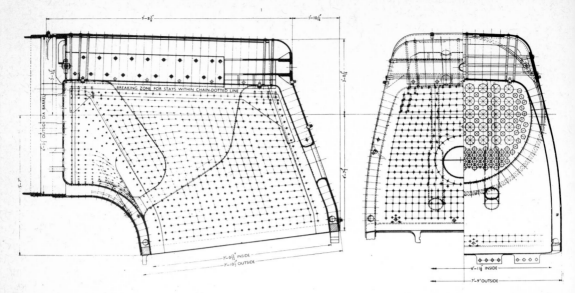

Fig 17
Welded steel inside and outside fireboxes of the SR
Merchant Navy Pacifics, showing location of the two
thermic syphons. Inner firebox plates $\frac{3}{8}$in thick. Net
volume of inner firebox and combustion chamber about
275 cu ft. Firedoor was steam operated

the crank webs, more conveniently with built-up
crank axles, though Bury is credited with beginning
the practice in forged axles on the London & Birmingham by 1845. Only Drummond on LSWR
4-4-0 and 0-4-4T locomotives from 1903 to 1911,
beginning with the 395-class 4-4-0 seems to have
carried this idea to the pitch where weights in the
wheels were considered unnecessary, crankweb
prolongations countering both revolving and
reciprocating masses.

Four-cylinder locomotives with 180° cranks had
almost self-balancing reciprocating masses.
However, after Wilson's engine of 1825 no four-
cylinder non-articulated locomotives saw service in
this country until the conversion of NBR 4-4-0 No
224 to a tandem compound in 1885 and of two
similar arrangements on the GWR in 1886, but all
these were two-crank engines. The first four-
cylinder engines with both inside and outside cranks
were Webb's compound 4-4-0s on the LNWR and
the Manson simple-expansion 4-4-0 on the GSWR,
both in 1897. Manson's object may have been better
balance, though the existing inside-cylinder 4-4-0s
on the GSWR rode as well as any inside-cylinder
4-4-0s. Four-cylinder engines with the 135° crank
setting to get a more even torque and more equable
blast on the fire (North Stafford 0-6-0T of 1922 and
SR Lord Nelson 4-6-0 in 1926) could be balanced
satisfactorily.

Like four-cylinder types, three-cylinder engines
were better balanced in regard to longitudinal forces
than two-cylinder forms, so much so that Bulleid
did not balance any portion of the reciprocating
weight in his SR Pacifics and the engines did not
suffer thereby at any speed up to the 95-100mph
they reached occasionally. It was the balancing
aspect, and not more even torque or greater power,
that led to the first three-cylinder locomotives, built
in 1847 at Newcastle in accordance with the
Stephenson-Howe patent No 11086 of 1846. Here
the two outside cylinders had cranks on the same
centre line, with the inside crank at right angles to
them. These two locomotives were long-boiler
2-2-2-0s for the York, Newcastle & Berwick, but one
of them made some trips on the Southern Division
of the LNWR in 1847. The idea behind this was
tried also on a two-cylinder engine with cranks at
the same angle by Sinclair on the ECR in 1856, but
the uncertain starting and uneven torque made the
experiment brief.

Next three-cylinder engine was a mineral 0-6-0
built in the shops of the Blyth & Tyne Railway in
1868 under John Kendal, but here the reason was to
get greater power and more even torque, for the
cylinders were of normal diameter whereas the three
cylinders of the 1847 engines had a combined
volume scarcely more than that of the standard
two-cylinder long-boiler 2-2-2-0s of the time. For
home use three-cylinder simple-expansion propulsion was not applied again until the end of 1902, in
the GER 0-10-0T, which was a very definite
attempt to get even torque and high accelerative
capacity, but three-cylinder compounds of Webb
type were running from 1882.

68

# 9 *The Infinite Variety*

The go-as-you-please attitude characteristic of many aspects of Victorian life led on the railways to a collection of locomotives beyond individual imagination. Between 1855 and 1895 over 200 locomotive superintendents held office on English, Scottish and Welsh railways. Each had his individual style and likes and was not constrained to follow anything done by his predecessor; he often changed simply to show he had tenets of his own, and the locomotive committee of the board did nothing to restrain him. Each of these men in his time was responsible for anything from one to a dozen locomotive classes to

his own requirements, and if money was tight he might have to build or rebuild from parts in stock or from old engines, and 'so many locomotives, so many classes' became the basis.

Until the 1870s specifications were rarely binding as to details, and private builders added their own practices, such as Beyer Peacock brass pistons. Off the LNWR few attempts were made at parts standardisation between different classes, for away from that system no railway chairman had a passion for ordered economy, though parsimony was rife and unplanned changes in permitted expenditure congenital. Added to this, few locomotives had a life under 25 years and commonly lasted through the tenure of two or three superintendents. Thus the whole locomotive scene became one of infinite variety — and kaleidoscopic variety, for design, construction, details, size, appearance and colour were ever-changing, so much so that mention can be made only of a few notable examples.

With the infinite variety went distinctly finite efficiency. Adoption of expansion valve motions from

Fig 18
The 12 Large Hawthorns were the principal express engines of the GNR through the first dozen years after the opening of the direct King's Cross-York line in 1852. Nine of them had Hawthorn domes; the other three had domeless boilers, Hawthorn perforated dry pipe, and regulator in the smokebox as shown here. They were among the first double-frame engines to have end-to-end inside frames. Transverse midfeather in firebox

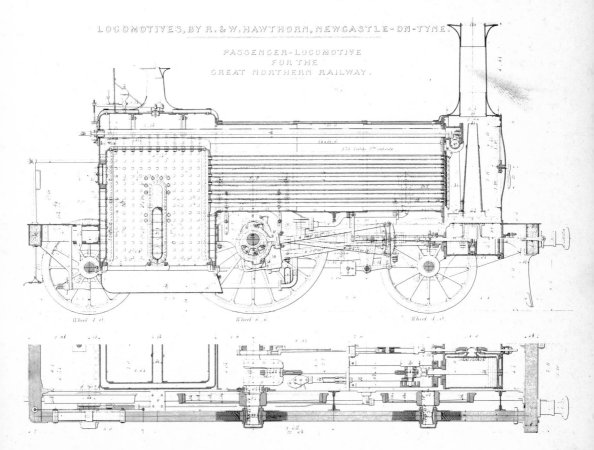

LOCOMOTIVES, BY R. & W. HAWTHORN, NEWCASTLE-ON-TYNE.

PASSENGER-LOCOMOTIVE
FOR THE
GREAT NORTHERN RAILWAY.

Crampton *Kinnaird* by Tulk & Ley in 1847 for the
Dundee, Perth & Aberdeen Jct, as running in the early
1860s. (R. E. Bleasdale)

1840-3 gave a pronounced enhancement in free running and power, but proportions were little understood. By 1860, when around 5500 locomotives
were at work on UK railways, the great majority
were wheezing and clanking along on passenger
trains rarely more than twice the weight of engine
and tender; and by the same token around half of
the whole power generated in the cylinders was being absorbed in propelling engine and tender along
the level and uphill. Only with the production of
engines such as the DX 0-6-0s on the LNWR and
the Sturrock 0-6-0s (with and without steam
tenders) on the GNR did any marked improvement
come as a result of bigger boilers and cylinders and
better manufacture.

Anything from 12 to 18lb coke/mile were consumed in getting the engine-tender combination
along the line. The machines themselves were not
responsible entirely for such figures; the track contributed its share, and one well-known engineer of
the Stephenson school, G. P. Bidder, felt in 1860
that 'none of our lines are safe at speeds above
30mph'. Many sections of line were still on stone
blocks as late as 1854-5.

Nor were locomotives worked particularly hard.
As late as 1863-4 Ramsbottom repeatedly told his
board that 'no engine stock can be worked with
proper economy when the duty per engine in stock
exceeds 50 engine-miles or 4100 ton-miles per day'.
Daily mileage per engine in stock on the LNWR rose

from 46 and ton-mileage from 3985 in 1858 to 54.3
and 5080 in 1864, and these would be good averages
for the time. Of course main-line locomotives gave
more. From 1858 through runs from Liverpool and
Crewe to Carlisle began, the crews lodging overnight at Carlisle; in 1858-9 there were through
workings on mineral and goods trains from Preston
to Bushbury, Bescot and Rugby, involving round
trips of 206 to 256 miles, going out one day and
returning the next, or later the same day. On the
GNR, passenger locomotives began through runs
from London to Grantham in 1862, and yearly
averages of the best types were around 28,000 miles,
but Sturrock considered main-line freight engines
should not much exceed 20,000 miles a year.

The infinite variety came partly from the increase
in the number of works building locomotives from
the time of the 1844-5 Railway Mania. At least 16
different works began building steam locomotives
between 1844 and 1855, and another 18 of those
dating back before 1844 were still in business and
had their own styles and ideas that were allowed
much scope. Further, at least a dozen railway works
were building new engines. Nevertheless, a few
years after the Mania, demand had fallen well below
productive capacity and there was a period of price
cutting, losses and failures that involved, among
other events, the disappearance in 1857-8 of one of
the largest builders, E. B. Wilson, before growing
industrialisation brought greater demand and the
founding of still further works, mainly for industrial
and small locomotives.

Constructionally most locomotives came within
one or other of the five main groups outlined in

Chapter 5, but there were exceptions, including two 0-4-0 tender locomotives *Fire Queen* and *Jenny Lind* (not *the* Jenny) that violated every canon of locomotive design. Undue publicity has often been accorded freak types like the Cramptons and *Cornwall* in its original state, and the Cramptons must be considered as quite unconventional even though 320 tender engines were built altogether, of which only 39 were built in Britain, 32 of them being for British railways.

One extraordinary type that did do good work over years was the 4-2-4T class with 9ft wheels and 6in wide flangeless treads on the 7ft gauge Bristol & Exeter (BER). Eight were built in 1853-4 by Rothwell and four were rebuilt in 1868-73 with the same wheel arrangement. Three of the rebuilds were again reconstructed in 1877 as 8ft flanged-wheel 4-2-2 tender engines at Swindon after the GWR had taken over the BER. As built the 9-footers had outside boxes with horns and guides up-turned for the driving axle, plus further bearings just inside the wheels. Rubber springs were above each, and their pillars were cross-equalised by a short beam just above the wheel top, and the pivot bracket of which

Bristol & Exeter 4-2-4T of 1853 as rebuilt in 1873. 9ft flangeless driving wheels; rubber cross-compensated springs. It is depicted as running on the GWR in 1876.

was rivetted to the boiler. Two smaller home-built 4-2-4Ts dating from 1859-61 were among the first engines to be given injectors and were early examples with a screw reverse gear, in this case with a pedal-operated locking for each of several chosen cut-off positions.

Apart from the Rainhill *Novelty* and the succeeding Braithwaite & Ericsson *William IV* and *Queen Adelaide*, tank engines began with two 2-2-0T Forresters on the London & Greenwich in 1836-7, the first London suburban locomotives. Then came a gap until 1842-3 when McConnell converted to the first saddle tanks two or three of the American Norris 4-2-0s of the Birmingham & Gloucester to get extra adhesion for the 1 in 37 Lickey incline. A single 30-ton six-coupled tank for this work was built in the B & G shops at Bromsgrove in 1845 and a year later came three inside-cylinder 2-2-2-2Ts by Vulcan for the Waterford & Kilkenny Railway. Outside-cylinder tank locomotives by Sharp Bros and Fairbairn were produced in 1847, and in 1848 came the first of the well-known Crewe-type 2-2-2Ts built by Jones & Potts for the London & Blackwall to supersede the original rope haulage.

Two broad-gauge 4-4-0STs, *Corsair* and *Brigand*, built at Swindon in 1849 to work the South Devon Railway were followed by 12 similar engines from

four different makers for the same line in 1851-3 and by 13 engines from Hawthorn for the GWR in 1854-5, and as late as 1866 the BER got a final 10 from Vulcan in which the Gooch motion of the South Devon and GWR engines was replaced by Allan straight link motion. Along with the first Crewe-built tank (a 2-4-0T for the steep Mold branch in 1849) and two Sharp Bros 2-4-0Ts for the Monmouthshire Railway[48] the same year, *Corsair* and *Brigand* were the first four-coupled tanks. With the Fairbairn and Crewe-type 2-4-0T on the Oldham and Chequerbent inclines and the Crampton dummy-crankshaft 0-4-0T that worked the 1 in 30 Folkestone harbour incline in the late 1850s, nearly all the engines just mentioned were for steep-grade working.

Table 5[49] shows an analysis of 1000 locomotive failures and defects in 1850-1 on the 587 engines of the LNWR Northern and Southern Divisions and the other lines worked, such as the Chester & Holyhead and Lancaster & Carlisle. About 200 of these engines would be Crewe-type 2-2-2s and 2-4-0s. Burst and leaking tubes were by far the largest single cause of failure, and except in good water districts they remained high on the list of defects until the end of steam. The table shows how undeveloped were certain parts which in later years showed only occasional defects. The big number of broken valve spindles and broken or lost eccentric straps and bolts may have been due to the high proportion of engines with the old Crewe indirect form of link motion and the short-rod pump drive off the backward eccentric strap.[50]

Carefully considered, the table illuminates how far locomotive design and manufacture had progressed in the 20 years from *Planet*. Bearing brasses in rods were still held by straps, gibs and cotters, though the gib was the only means of preventing the opening out of the strap through centrifugal force, and not until the mid-1850s came the solid end with an opening for the two halves of the brasses and a single large cotter. Split pins and split cotters were unknown until 1848-50. The first solid-bushed ends for coupling rods were introduced by Ramsbottom in 1866, that is not until he had got Crewe workmanship and procedure to a much higher standard than he found them in 1857.

Only a few Crewe-type tanks were built new. The most notable were the 2-2-2Ts with 6ft 6in wheels for express traffic on the ECR in 1854 — the first locomotives to be built at the then new Stratford works that replaced the original ECR repair establishment at Romford. These had the modified Crewe framing previously used by J. V. Gooch on the LSWR, in which the horn plates were bolted on. From 1859 to 1880 over a hundred Crewe-type 2-4-0 tender engines on the LNWR were converted

to side tanks of the same axle layout and were used for local passenger, freight and shunting duties. So economically minded were Ramsbottom and Webb that the tanks and bunker were made up from the scrapped tender superstructures and retained the flared tops. Another 26 engines were converted to saddle tanks.

Growth of London from the late 1850s brought an up-surge in tank engine construction for urban and suburban work, supplemented by a growing use for miscellaneous duties in the provinces. Tank engines for shunting were a later feature, as were tank engines in industry, and some of the earliest of the latter were crane types. The rise in public works and growth of the steel industry at home and abroad brought several new manufacturers specialising in small tank engines, and three, Manning Wardle, Hudswell Clarke and Hunslet, were set up next door to each other on land that had belonged to E. B. Wilson's Railway Foundry. This was the beginning of makers' 'standard' engines prominent in industrial practice until the end.

The 40 years from 1855-60 were the heyday of the 4-4-0T in London traffic. They began with the Stephenson five for the North London in 1855, followed by six Hawthorn-built Crampton tanks for the South Eastern in 1857 and one or two Craven rebuilds on the LBSCR (1859-61), and then the Beyer-Fowler Met tanks of 1864, of which 120 were built for the Metropolitan and District railways from that year until 1886, which handled practically all the traffic on those two systems until electrification over the years 1900-07. Six similar engines for the Midland (1868) and 16 for the LNWR (1871-2) also worked in the London area, but another six for the LSWR went further afield. All 148 were built by Beyer Peacock, to whom most of the detail design was due.

Though developed while coal burning was becoming general, the Met engines until about 1870 burned coke to obviate a smoke nuisance, but coke had fumes of its own and South Wales semi-anthracite was substituted, the consumption of which at 34lb/mile was due to the peculiar conditions of the service. Most of the time the engines worked condensing, with no blast and with the exhaust led back to the water tanks, so that the blower was on almost continuously to keep the fire going.

On the NLR the inside-cylinder Stephenson design was enlarged and given a longer-wheelbase bogie from 1863, and in 1868 was changed over to what became the classic NLR outside-cylinder 4-4-0T that continued on some of the North London services until well after the 1923 Grouping. The last-built of the inside-cylinder form were the first to have side movement given to the bogie pivot, though concurrently in 1865 six 4-4-0 tender engines on the

**Table 5  Analysis of 1000 Locomotive Failures, LNWR, 1851-52 (587 Locos)**

| No | Description of Failure | No | Description of Failure |
|----|------------------------|----|------------------------|
| 157 | Burst and leaky tubes | 6 | Broken gibs |
| 92 | Broken springs[1] | 5 | Broken firebox stays |
| 89 | Broken valve spindles | 5 | Detached ashpans |
| 77 | Broken and defective pumps | 3 | Smokebox and chimney end fires |
| 48 | Broken feed pipes | 3 | Broken weigh-bar shaft brackets |
| 40 | Broken pistons and rods | 3 | Feed pipes stopped up; dropped fires |
| 34 | Broken and damaged valves and gear | 3 | Broken spring balances |
| 34 | Lost and broken bolts and pins | 3 | Broken slide blocks |
| 34 | Firebars burned out | 3 | Broken crank rods |
| 31 | Lost and broken cotters | 3 | Tubes drawn in, chimney end |
| 29 | Plugs and joints blown out | 3 | Broken axleboxes |
| 25 | Broken and lost eccentric straps | 3 | Broken slide valves |
| 21 | Broken wheels and tyres | 3 | Broken right-hand bearings |
| 21 | Broken and bent coupling and connecting rods | 3 | Broken glands |
| 17 | Broken axlebox sponge boxes[4] | 3 | Defective hose-pipes |
| 17 | Broken and bent eccentric rods | 3 | Broken piston rings[2] |
| 17 | Broken crankpins | 2 | Broken brakes |
| 15 | Broken and shifted eccentric sheaves | 2 | Lost quadrant washers |
| 13 | Broken crank and other axles | 2 | Broken cross-head spindles |
| 13 | Broken eccentric straps and bolts | 2 | Defective mudhole doors |
| 13 | Broken and damaged steam and suction pipes | 2 | Broken weighbar shafts |
| 13 | Broken and defective reversing levers | 2 | Broken driving-journal brasses |
| 11 | Broken connecting rod straps | 2 | Broken link-motion studs |
| 11 | Broken middle bearings[3] | 2 | Broken catches of firebars |
| 9 | Broken spring-bearings, screws and buckles | 2 | Broken glass tubes |
| 8 | Broken lifting links | 1 | Nut off tender drawbar |
| 7 | Broken blow-off and other cocks | 1 | Broken tender eye bolt |
| 6 | Broken quadrant studs | 1 | Defective whistle |
| 6 | Lost and loose regulator spindles | 1 | Boiler burst |
|  |  | 1000 | Total |

[1]  Much track was still on stone blocks  
[3]  In Patentee-type engines  

[2]  This was before the day of Ramsbottom split rings  
[4]  This type had been introduced at Crewe around 1850

GNSR were built with a similar arrangement. In neither case was any rubber or steel spring side control provided; that came only in 1869-70 and brought the William Adams bogie to its full evolution.

Coincident with the various larger 4-4-0Ts was developed the reversed or 0-4-4T, but though many 4-4-0Ts had outside cylinders the only 0-4-4Ts with that cylinder location were four on the Caledonian in 1873-4 and one Fairlie twin-bogie single-boiler engine in England in 1878. This wheel arrangement was developed out of the 0-4-2T, of which the London Chatham & Dover (LCDR) and GNR examples had the extraordinary distance of 11ft 9in and 12ft 9in between driving and trailing axles. Despite Bridges Adams radial boxes at the rear they could be hard riders.

First 0-4-4Ts were Cudworth's on the South Eastern derived in 1866 from his 0-4-2Ts of 1863-4. Both had outside frames and coupling-rod flycranks; but the 0-4-4Ts had the coupled springs equalised down each side to get three-point suspension and the large compensating beams outside the open splashers were prominent features. These engines had back tanks with all the water above the trailing bogie so there was minimum alteration in adhesion weight as water was used up. This layout applied to all 0-4-4Ts until Johnson's first side tanks on the GER in 1872 and his first batch on the Midland in 1875. On the latter line 26 back tanks

were already in service from 1869-70, with U-shaped tanks holding 1025gal, and were strongly built with iron frames 1in thick inside and $1\frac{1}{8}$in outside and driving axle journals $6\frac{3}{4}$in dia by 5in long inside and 6in by 8in outside. Not one of these Midland engines was scrapped before 1914 and the last one went in 1935.

Back tanks continued in new construction until the 1880s, for example to the BTP (bogie tank passenger) class on the NER, 124 of which were built between 1874 and 1883 by Neilson, Hawthorn, and the then three works of the NER at Gateshead, Darlington and York. They were the quintessence of go-as-you-please, for every one of the five works involved provided its own details and shades of colouring, and there were three variations in cylinder dimensions and two in wheel size. These were the engines chosen in 1903 to handle the autocar or push-and-pull trains on the NER with the engine between two coaches. From 1890 to 1921 around 60 were rebuilt as 0-6-0 side tanks and one or two hung on until the 1950s. Most of the others remained in 0-4-4T form until the 1920s and retained to the end the cigar-screw and lever reverse. One, No 957, was rebuilt in 1903 to 2-2-4T with a 19-ton axle load, heavier than any other NER engine of the time but exceeded after a few months by the first NER Atlantic, No 532; it was the last British single-driver to run in normal revenue service.

Through the 50 years from the first GER design, side-tank 0-4-4Ts were widely used on suburban and branch-line work, and even on semi-fasts on the NER and LSWR, but on the latter line they came under the stricture of Board of Trade inspecting officers for high speeds. Only the LNWR among large

Webb's three-cylinder compound 2-2-2-2 of the Greater Britain class, as painted cream with ornate lining for the Diamond Jubilee year of 1897. (British Railways)

24-ton Terrier 0-6-0T with 4ft wheels, of which 50 were built at the Brighton works of the LBSCR, 1872-80. Still with wooden brake blocks; birch brooms in front of guard irons for de-icing.

railways was not a user of this layout, though the GWR had only a small number and was not fortunate with them. Few 0-4-4Ts were built this century but over 700 came into possession of the Group companies in 1923, and the LMS added a few of Caledonian design and some of its own origination.

Rougher riders than 0-4-4Ts were 2-4-2Ts, but they were more numerous at the 1923 Grouping. The 'Lanky tank' was the most notable of all 2-4-2Ts; the first was the first engine to be completed at the then new Horwich works (1889) and from then until 1911 330 were built, all with Joy valve gear. By 1912 they were working 70 per cent of all LYR passenger-train mileage including many express services. Weight went up gradually from 56 to $66\frac{1}{2}$ tons, and the last-built batch had superheaters and $20\frac{1}{2}$in cylinders. Water pick-up gear was fitted to many. They had their times on the problematical list, especially in the early years of this century when they were put on to fast workings and encountered a minor epidemic of broken tyres, axleboxes, springs and derailments.

Successive locomotive superintendents of the GER from 1873 to 1912, and there were six, seemed unable to make up their minds as to the relative efficacy of the 0-4-4T and 2-4-2T and built numerous batches of each almost alternately. The 2-4-2T had come to the GER as early as 1864 with Sinclair's $36\frac{1}{2}$-ton outside-cylinder variety which had a Bissell truck (patented 1858) at the front and a rigidly-held axle at the rear. A lapse on the part of so sound an engineer as Sinclair was the attachment of the Bissell pivot bracket to the boiler. These Sinclair engines closely followed in time the initial 2-4-2T – the 41-ton inside-cylinder *White Raven* of the St Helen's Railway built in 1863 by Cross with a Bridges Adams radial axlebox at each end that gave an unsteady gait, and Bridges Adams spring steel inserts between rims and tyres. This was perhaps the only engine painted white, the nearest approaches to that colour otherwise being the cream with blue and gold lining the of the LNWR 2-2-2-2 *Queen Empress* in the Diamond Jubilee year 1897, and the cream of a Sinclair 2-2-2 for the honeymoon train of the Prince and Princess of Wales in 1863.

Most notable of all Victorian passenger tank engines were diminutive 0-6-0 side tanks – the Brighton Terriers and the GER suburbans. With the trains they handled, light in weight but not always so in relation to the 24 tons of engine weight, the Terriers from the beginning gained a reputation for acceleration and speed, though how they brought the trains of partly hand-braked four-wheelers to 172 stops averaging 0.8 miles apart in a working day of 17hr on the South London line passes comprehension, for until 1875 they had only a hand screw brake and wooden blocks. In much

One of the first (1880) batch of London, Tilbury &
Southend 4-4-2Ts, the first large-wheel tank engines.
The Westinghouse brake was a later addition.
(K. H. Leech collection)

later days, with the front set of coupling rods removed to give a 2-4-0T, they were timed along the South
Coast on one-coach push-and-pulls at fractionally
over 60mph, or 420rpm of the 4ft wheels. As with
all Stroudley's engines every detail was given
thought, and the small size plus the vitality of the
performance gained the 50 engines built from 1872
to 1880 a coterie still strong to this day, partly
because of the number preserved.

For hard slogging work on a much higher load
factor the Terriers were surpassed by the GER
0-6-0Ts that for 30 years from 1890 handled much
of the intensive suburban service centred on Liverpool Street station, particularly on the 11-mile route
to Enfield with 15 stops on an overall schedule of 40
min.

After trials in 1889 with an 0-6-0 shunting tank,
a new design specifically for Enfield services was
produced, similar to the shunters but with air-brake
equipment, crescent-balanced cast steel wheel centres in place of unbalanced cast iron, screw reverse
in place of lever, tanks put further forward, and
wheelbase increased by 6in. The $16\frac{1}{2}$in by 22in
cylinders, 4ft wheels and 140psi boiler pressure of
the shunters were retained. One hundred were built
from 1890 to 1901, but the last 20 had 160psi
pressure, and from 1894 most of the engines were

given simple condensing arrangements in the tanks.
In 1904 another 20 were built with 180psi boilers
and 1200gal tanks, and though heating surface
went up only 2 per cent the grate area was increased
by 17 per cent to 14.5sq ft. These 120 engines worked the greater part of the GER London suburban
services until the 0-6-2Ts began to appear in
numbers after World War I.

As notable in their way were the Tilbury tanks,
probably the largest tank engines in the country in
1880. They were for outer suburban work, and then
what was really fast interurban traffic as soon as the
Barking-Pitsea cut-off came into operation in 1888
and gave a through run to Southend. This outside–
cylinder 4-4-2T design was due to William Adams as
consultant, but the design was repeatedly enlarged
and strengthened until 1909 by the Whiteleggs,
father and son, who were the only locomotive
superintendents the LTSR had from taking over its
own working in 1880 until the absorption by the
Midland in 1912. The initial batch weighed 56 tons
and cost £1970 apiece; the last delivery scaled 72
tons and cost £3224 each; and of the 94 locomotives
ordered by the Tilbury from first to last 70 were
outside-cylinder 4-4-2Ts.[51] Surprisingly in view of
the number of inside cylinders favoured after 1880,
the 4-4-2T with cylinders between the frames did
not come until 1888, first on the Taff Vale.

Most characteristic of all Victorian passenger
engines were the single-drivers built to a dozen
different wheel arrangements. The 2-2-2 was the
most numerous and has been given some attention

in Chapter 5. In true bogie form the 4-2-2 was not seen until 1870, for the broad-gauge Iron Dukes did not have a bogie, nor did GNR No 215 as built in 1853 at a cost of £3500 by Hawthorn to Sturrock's requirements for an engine to run easily at 60-65 mph and to cover 100 miles without stopping. Only the GNSR among larger systems never used a single-driver, and it was at the bottom of the 'large' scale.

After *Rocket* Patrick Stirling's 8-footer 4-2-2s[52] were probably the best-known locomotives of the 19th Century, and were the most successful engines built that had no direct mechanical engineering influence on practice elsewhere or on later locomotives of the owning company. Additional to the 8ft driving wheels, the general size and cylinder capacity (18in by 28in) of No 1 were well in advance of other single-drivers existing in 1870. No other 4-2-2 engines were then at work, and the most powerful standard-gauge 2-2-2s of the time were Conner's 8ft 2in engines on the Caledonian, the Sinclair class on the GER, and the Armstrong Swindon-built type on the GWR, cylinders in which did not exceed $17\frac{1}{4}$in by 24in.

Like most other large single-drivers the 8-footers were notable for steady uphill performance rather than for super speed; in fact only two single-driver classes were ever authentically timed above 83mph. The Stirlings were not one of the two, yet for some 15 years they and the same engineer's 7ft 6in 2-2-2s built from 1885 to 1894 were the mainstays of GNR express traffic when that line was commonly accepted as the fastest in Britain. There was little to choose between the daily performance of the two classes, but an 8-footer was usually selected for anything special.

In one respect this unique class was thoroughly representative of the Victorian locomotive scene in that not one of the 53 engines was exactly the same as any one of the other 52. Stirling's boilers were small for the cylinder size though perhaps not when

One of the 80 GWR outside-frame 7ft 8in 4-2-2s of the 1890s, 50 of which were built new and 30 rebuilt from 2-2-2s. They were a typical example of the resuscitation of the large single-driver 1886-1901. (British Railways)

the small number of strokes per minute are considered; but Stirling, under pressure from the GNR board, was economically minded and his engines were so attuned to the duties that the boiler could furnish just enough steam to surmount at good speed the 12- and 20-mile rises to Potters Bar and Stoke northbound and then run under easy steam the rest of the way from London to York at 50-53mph average with the train loads of the time.

The impact of the 8-footers on the publicity sense of the 1870s and 1880s was enhanced in that from 1868 to 1881 the single-driver was almost in eclipse for new construction, only the GWR and LBSCR building single-drivers for top-class traffic except for a batch of 10 on the GER in 1879 which, like the Stirlings, were unusual for the time in having outside cylinders and inside frames. The other outstanding single-driver design of the 1870s was Stroudley's 2-2-2 class on the LBSCR with inside cylinders, inside frames and inside axleboxes throughout. The design was introduced in 1874, but 24 out of the 26 engines were built in 1880-2 after the first large 0-4-2 had been set to work. They worked the Brighton line to Portsmouth for years, and on withdrawal in 1907-9 most of them had gone not far short of a million miles.

Construction of four-coupled express passenger engines continued unabated except for the unexplained return of Charles Sacré to large Crewe-type 2-2-2s on the MSL in 1882-3. Then a sudden resuscitation of single-drivers, almost entirely in 4-2-2 form, began with the Edinburgh Exhibition engine of 1886 – Caledonian No 123. The next year Derby began to build 4-2-2s with 7ft 4in wheels which set a fashion, and from 1887 to 1901 over 230 large 4-2-2s were introduced on six major railways exclusive of the GNR. Unlike the 8-footers every one of them had inside cylinders and every one was built in a railway workshop; 25 of them had piston valves when new and another 10 had them when rebuilt; one of the GCR engines was even superheated when reboilered and was the only single-driver to be so equipped. On three lines (Midland, GER, GWR) a return was made to double frames with outside boxes for the trailing wheels and both inside and outside boxes for the driving axles. A score of NER engines were

two-cylinder compounds when built and 10 on the GER were oil burners. The J-class on the NER had the largest pair of inside cylinders ever seen in England, 20in hp and 28in lp. The six engines of the GCR were the only single-drivers to be built new with Belpaire fireboxes, but several of the GWR 4-2-2s had them on rebuilding.

The revival is always said to have begun with an effective means of steam sanding devised by Charles Holt (a nephew of Ramsbottom) at Derby works which was appreciated by his chief, S. W. Johnson, to the extent that 95 single-drivers were turned out of Derby 1887-1900. But the earlier Caledonian No 123 had efficient air sanding worked off the Westinghouse brake supply; and there is evidence that before Holt's invention Johnson was considering a new single-driver as a result of the performance of an old Kirtley 2-2-2 brought back on to main-line work to cope with a temporary power shortage. The idea of steam sanding was not new. It had been advocated by S. E. Peal[53] in 1862, along with a suggestion that the sand might be carried between the dome and the dome casing to keep it warm and dry. The latter part of Peal's suggestion was adopted by Martley on 2-4-0s for the LCDR in 1866, but with gravity drop.

The big 4-2-2s of the last 15 years of the 19th Century became practicable because of increasing rail weights that could take 18 to 19 tons axle load (Stirling's last 8-footers of 1895 had 20 tons), and because of the realisation that a properly proportioned single-driver had good adhesion propensities. This was the one avenue along which the GNR 8-footers may have influenced extraneous practice for their daily performances had been observed from 1870. The trains at first given all these engines were not light for the time, but from the turn of the century loads quickly became too great for any single-driver, though at a later stage some of the Midland 4-2-2s showed occasional ability to haul 300-ton trains on the London–Nottingham main line where ruling grades were not steeper than 1 in 140.

Single-driver speed reached its culmination in the GWR type and the NER class J. The latter were properly timed to reach 85mph both as compounds and when rebuilt as simples. The GWR 4-2-2 *Duke of Connaught* was reputed to have exceeded 91mph on the record Ocean Mail run of 9 May 1904, but the intermediate timings scarcely support more than 88-89mph; on the estimated coal consumption of 3500lb between Bristol and London the firing rate was 110lb/sfg/hr, probably never approached on any other single-driver.

While the single-driver was in abeyance through the 1870s the 2-4-0 was the principal passenger type in new construction, for the time of the 4-4-0 was not yet. The 2-4-0 axle layout began with a Tayleur

(Vulcan)-built engine in 1835 for Belgium. Few others were built for the next 10 years, after which the 2-4-0 went through many inside and outside cylinder and inside and outside frame variations before it arrived at the express passenger stage in the late 1860s. As usual, coming events cast their shadows before, in the shape of J. Beattie's and R. Sinclair's outside-cylinder express 2-4-0s on the LSWR and ECR respectively from 1859.

In general the 2-4-0s of the 1870s had inside frames throughout or inside frames carrying the coupled axleboxes plus outside frames taking the leading boxes; but the Caledonian had Crewe-type engines with 7ft 1in wheels. Many had long lives, in particular those with strong iron frame structures like the Kirtley engines on the Midland and the 901 and 1440 classes on the NER. Some of each lasted into Grouping days and the NER 901 type had by then covered around $1\frac{1}{4}$ million miles each.

Of all 2-4-0s the Webb Precedents of the LNWR were best known and made the most noise, for they were hard worked. Continuous development of inside-cylinder inside-frame 2-4-0s was effected at Crewe from Ramsbottom's Samson class in 1863 through the Newtons (6ft 7in wheels) in 1866, the Webb Precursors (5ft 6in) of 1874, the Webb Precedents (6ft 7in) in 1874, and the construction of another set of Precedents in the 1890s to take the place, numbers and names of the 1874-82 engines that had worn themselves out with hard and fast haulage. Limited cut-off came long before Gresley's 65 per cent of the early 1920s; Ramsbottom's Newtons had 67 per cent maximum, and Webb's Precursors had only 56 per cent. All the Ramsbottom 2-4-0s had Stephenson motion; Webb used the Allan straight-link form for his, but the period of patent royalties was then past, and Webb seemed willing to pay patent royalties only to Joy, and his motion was never applied by Webb to express 2-4-0s.

For 20 years from 1860 with one exception the outside-cylinder 4-4-0s built were failures or near failures for reasons unconnected with the axle layout. The one successful design was that introduced on the GNSR in 1861 which worked soundly and unobtrusively.

The only exceptions to the outside-cylinder location in 4-4-0s built down to 1871 were the small Whitby Bogies on the NER (1864) which had inside cylinders, outside frames and short wheelbase bogies, and similar rebuilds in the 1860s of five Crampton dummy-crankshaft 4-2-0s on the LCDR which retained their original short-base pivoting-only bogies. Up to the mid-1870s a long-base bogie was provided on tender engines only when outside cylinders had to be cleared, yet the short-base swivelling-only types were little use in guiding and were a menace on derailment.

Outside-cylinder 4-4-0 with 5ft wheels built in 1861 for the Great North of Scotland Railway by Robert Stephenson & Co.

Robert Stephenson & Co was closely associated with most of the very early standard-gauge 4-4-0s beginning with the NLR 4-4-0Ts in 1855 and building the first two SDR types (1860-1), the GNSR engines (1861-2), the Whitby Bogies (1864), and the LCDR 4-2-0s that were rebuilt to 4-4-0s. Possibly this was due to an effort to push the primitive short-wheelbase pivoting bogie.

Prior to 1880 appeared three further classes of outside-cylinder 4-4-0s that were failures – the W. G. Beattie engines on the LSWR in 1876 because of over-cylindering, frame cracks, and the fitting of piston valves that gave no escape for entrapped water; the Caledonian No 128 class in 1877 because of grates and boilers much too small for the main-line fasts they were built to work; and the Adams engines on the GER in 1876 mainly because they were too heavy. However, in the 1870s Adams completely rebuilt 20 Sinclair outside-cylinder 2-4-0s into successful general purpose 4-4-0s. On the Highland Crewe-type 4-4-0s were developed from 1873, and for the conditions in the far north they proved sound and adequate and were built until 1898, the heaviest, in 1892, scaling 45 tons.

The first really successful outside-cylinder inside–frame 4-4-0s were the Adams type introduced on the LSWR 1879-80, and all that engineer's 4-4-0s thereafter were of similar formation with 5ft 7in, 6ft 7in and 7ft 1in wheels, and with the added advantage of a 7ft 6in wheelbase for the Adams bogie with spring-controlled side play. In 1882 the design was scaled down for engines on the Lynn & Fakenham, later absorbed into the Midland & Great Northern Joint, which had 17in by 24in cylinders, 6ft wheels, and 38 tons weight contrasted with the 18in and 19in cylinders and 45 to 50 tons weight of the LSWR machines.

However by the time Adams had got to that stage the classic inside-cylinder inside-frame 4-4-0 was established, and, as steel manufacture improved, crank axles became more reliable, and engines big for the time could be built on 1in steel frames, whereas the outside-cylinder types just mentioned had $1\frac{1}{8}$in and $1\frac{1}{4}$in frames of iron. First of the inside-cylinder inside-frame 4-4-0s were two in 1871 on the NBR produced under Thomas Wheatley, who at one time had been at Wolverton on the Southern Division of the LNWR. One of the two, No 224, went down in the Tay Bridge disaster in 1879, was fished out of the Firth and repaired, continued to run as a two-cylinder simple until rebuilt as a tandem compound with 13in and 20in cylinders, all inside, in 1885, and after a year or two in that guise became once again a two-cylinder simple and remained in that form until withdrawal in 1919.

James Stirling on the neighbouring GSWR was the next to build the type, with 21 domeless-boiler

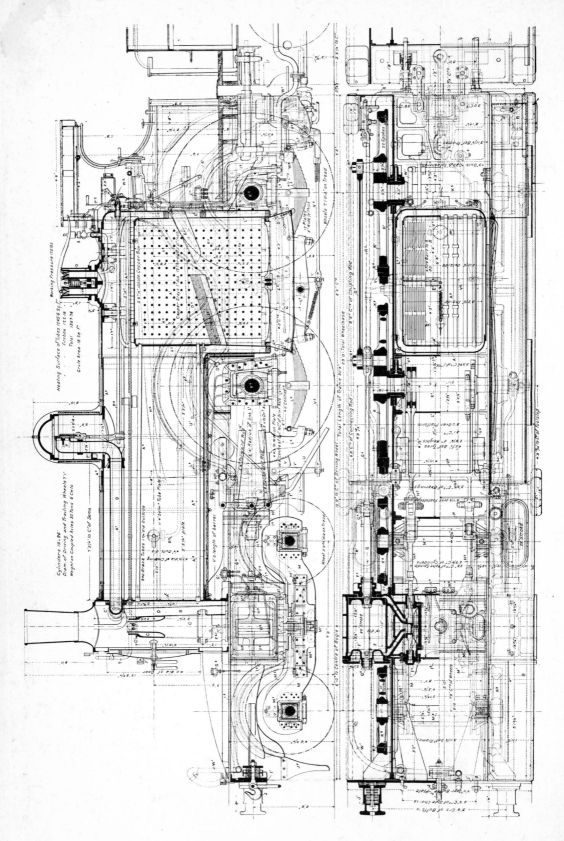

Fig 19
The Adams outside-cylinder engines with 7ft 1in wheels of the 1880s and 1890s were among the most free running and successful 4-4-0s of the 19th century

engines introduced between 1873 and 1877, the last 20 of which had steam reversing gear. Johnson designed two 4-4-0s for the GER in 1873 but they were not completed until 1874, by which time he had joined the Midland. This delay may have been due to the means of construction, for the boilers were built at Stratford, the cylinders, motion and driving rods by Beyer Peacock, and the frames and wheels by Neilson. For the first two years these engines also ran with iron inside fireboxes; no tenders were built for them and they received two old ones. On the Midland Johnson enlarged his GER design, but being then with a richer company he could order 10 straight off from Kitson, and they were set to work 1876-7 between Derby and Manchester.

From this time the 4-4-0 had an assured place, and formed the greater part of new express passenger construction until 10-wheelers of 4-4-2 and 4-6-0 notations began to appear in 1898-1900.

Stroudley express 0-4-2 Gladstone class of the LBSCR. The engine shown gained a gold medal (second class) at the Paris exhibition 1889. (Museum of British Transport)

The popularity of the type was probably enhanced by the standard of performance put up on the NBR and Caledonian by Drummond engines from 1876 onwards, and the five Scottish railways were proportionately greater users than the English lines though James Stirling took his domeless-boiler design to the South Eastern. The 4-4-0s he built at Ashford from 1882 were of sound design and performance, so sound that those coming into SR stock on Grouping in 1923 were considered to be more worth retaining for secondary-line services than the remaining examples of one of the most outstanding designs of late Victorian years – the Stroudley Gladstones of the LBSCR.

Stroudley had begun on the Brighton with 2-4-0s having outside frames and outside bearings for all axles, but from 1875 he reversed the whole layout for express engines and produced in 1878-80 the six Richmond-class 0-4-2s, and in 1882 enlarged this design into the Gladstones. He gave excellent reasons for all aspects of the 0-4-2 layout, and in his careful hands it was quite suitable for the LBSCR on which speeds rarely exceeded 60-65mph in pre-1914 years. In daily working these apparently simple engines were economical, but they were rather heavy on crank axles and cylinder castings, both costly items, and the building price at £52/ton of empty engine and tender weight was high in the 1880s and above that of many 4-4-0s built in railway shops. Gladstone cylinders sloped down to

Typical British inside-cylinder inside-frame 0-6-0 of late Victorian years, the Midland Johnson type as built by Dubs. (Mitchell Library)

the driving axle at 1 in 11½; the slide valves were underneath and sloped up at 1 in 15, and the leading axle lay between the piston rod and valve spindle, the reverse of the original 0-4-2s of 1834 in which the cylinder was inclined upwards and the piston rod lay beneath the axle.

Major factor against Gladstone design was that no further development in size and power was practicable and the great majority of 0-4-2s before and after *Gladstone* – and there were many – were much less powerful and were engaged on quite secondary passenger workings, or, in Scotland, on local mineral trains for which small-wheel outside-cylinder types were favourites after the days of the Hawthorn inside-cylinder sandwich-frame standards of the 1840s and 1850s.

Though the eight-wheel engine in 4-2-2 and 4-4-0 forms became well established for main-line passenger work, the six-wheeler in 0-6-0 layout continued for even the heaviest freight and mineral trains. The rare exceptions were the Adams-Bromley 46-ton 2-6-0s on the GER in 1878; two 0-8-0 tender engines on the Barry Railway in 1889 that had been built for Scandinavia as some of the last engines built at Sharp Stewart's Manchester works; and, at the very end of the Century, the 80 Moguls obtained from North America by the Midland, GNR and GCR. The last-named engines were small and scarcely up to the power of large home-built 0-6-0s weighing around 42 tons, but delivery was six months quicker than offered by any British maker. The 42-ton 0-6-0s of that time were no more than 5 per cent in weight above the Stirling 0-6-0s on the GNR in 1871, and they themselves were no more powerful than the preceding Sturrock steam tender engines.

These last were an attempt to deal with rapidly increasing coal traffic and reduce the over-working of the existing 0-6-0s by running heavier trains. After a trial conversion in 1863 a total of 50 new-built tenders appeared in 1864-6 with two 12in by

17in cylinders driving a centre crank axle and with outside coupling rod connections bringing an 0-6-0 layout. Construction cost was not excessive for prices ran only from £2950 to £3250 per engine and tender at a time when the GNR was paying the same amount for 2-4-0 express engines with normal tenders. The tender-engine exhaust went through feedwater heating tubes in the tender before being discharged upwards at the back.

However they were awkward to handle, often enveloped the footplate in steam, were expensive to maintain, were greatly disliked by crews, and may eventually have led to the acceptance of Sturrock's resignation. Repair cost per mile per engine and tender was 20 per cent above that of a normal combination, not only because of work on the tenders but because the higher steam demand on the boilers brought greater wear in firebox plates and tubes. Full use could not be made of the higher tractive capacity because of the lengths of storage sidings and running loops, and the blocking of the celebrated level crossings in Lincoln city. From the beginning of 1867 the tender propulsive mechanism was removed gradually.

Yet it is strange how the coal traffic from South Yorkshire and Notts to London led three out of four successive superintendents into errors of proportion. Stirling's 0-6-0s of 1871-4 also were too powerful for the work that could be done and had not enough brake power for the loads they could haul. Then in 1925 Gresley produced his two three-cylinder booster-fitted 2-8-2s (thus repeating the principle of Sturrock's steam tenders) which had to have special paths diagrammed for them to take the 1600-ton trains they were capable of handling, and even then those trains had to be divided on a running line outside Ferme Park (London) before they could be dealt with in the yard. Lack of braking on the wagons prevented the power being used to haul lighter trains faster.

A feature of the years 1880-1900 was the attention paid to compounding, and this resolved itself into two main streams, the Webb system on the LNWR and the Worsdell-von Borries two-cylinder method on the GER and NER and, for a longer period though on a smaller scale, on the Belfast & Northern Counties, later the Northern Counties Committee, or NCC, of the Midland and LMS. One can say that even the two-cylinder form had some roots in Crewe for it was there, as works manager, that T. W. Worsdell had to do with Webb compounds in their very first stage. Webb's interest stemmed immediately and directly from the early work of Anatole Mallet.

Unfortunately Webb handicapped his engines from the beginning by an unskilful application of compounding, and for 15 years by dividing the drives from high-pressure and low-pressure cylinders to uncoupled axles in a succession of 2-2-2-0 and 2-2-2-2 engines. This uncoupled principle had been proposed for single-expansion engines first by Dawes in a patent of 1872, and in that form was applied on the LSWR by Drummond from 1897, but for compounds Mallet had recommended coupling the axles driven by the different cylinder groups.

Webb engines became a byword for ineffectiveness maintained by obstinacy; but though they had prominent idiosyncrasies the larger three-cylinder compounds (apart from the John Hicks) for several years made from 38,000 to 42,000 miles a year each,[54] and the Jeanie Deans class of 10 for some years averaged nearly 60,000 miles a year per loco, an astonishing figure for that time. The

First 4-6-0s to run in Britain were the 15 56-ton Jones goods engines of the Highland, 1894. (S. A. Forbes)

trouble with the smaller engines was that soon after Webb put the first ones in hand train weights started to go up more rapidly and he was unable to keep pace with the demands as long as the wheels were uncoupled, and for much of the mileage a pilot had to be provided for haulage as much as to ensure certain starting from stations and signal stops, for nearly all the three-cylinder passenger engines were main-line types. This more than nullified any economy in coal consumption that might have come from compounding. The pilot was always a single-expansion engine. The four-cylinder compound 0-8-0s and 4-4-0s were better and for a year or two probably measured up to the performance of the single-expansion engines running on most English lines; but the number of compounds in any case hardly rose above 12 per cent of LNWR stock and most of the traffic was handled by extremely effective Webb and Ramsbottom two-cylinder simples.

Starting was also a difficulty with the Worsdell two-cylinder compounds largely because of an automatic starting valve dependent on receiver pressure that could change the working over to compound too quickly and stall the locomotive, which it did as least as often as Webb's uncoupled engines spun their wheels in opposite directions. Once under way the two-cylinder compounds were good runners, and had what is not always appreciated, a more even turning moment throughout a wheel revolution than a two-cylinder simple. Worsdell began his compounding when on the GER with

83

eleven 4-4-0s, but most of his productions were on the NER between 1885 and 1892 and included 4-2-2 and 4-4-0 passenger engines, 0-6-0 goods engines and 0-6-2Ts totalling respectively 20, 37, 171 and 51. All the passenger engines were converted to simples by 1900 but the last conversions of the 0-6-0s were not done until 1912-14.

These Worsdell two-cylinder compounds led indirectly to the next and most effective stage of English compounding, the three-cylinder Smith system. The transition stage was NER 4-4-0 No 1619 built as a two-cylinder compound in 1893 and rebuilt as a three-cylinder compound in 1898 to the ideas of W. M. Smith, then chief draughtsman at Gateshead works. No more three-cylinder compounds were built by the NER but the principles were applied in 1901-2 by Johnson on the Midland, who for some years had been using Smith's piston valves. This was the beginning of the Midland 4-4-0 compounds built under Johnson, Deeley and Fowler, and then adopted by the LMS as the principal four-coupled express passenger type. They had the advantages of compounds, of which in English practice greater ratios of expansion and coal economy were not pronounced; in fact the advantages were mechanical rather than thermal. From 1906-7 Deeley put in a starting and intercepting valve of his own so that the engines were Deeley's compounds rather than Smith's.

From this infinite variety arising in Victorian times the locomotive tableau in the 1890s began to change and to move in two directions: first a concentration on fewer general types, and, second, a substantial increase in size. In the first aspect more and more top-class passenger traffic came to be handled by inside-cylinder inside-frame 4-4-0s and goods traffic by 0-6-0s of similar cylinder and frame location. First appreciable increase in size was foreshadowed by the Jones 4-6-0s on the Highland in 1894 though engine alone was only 7 tons more in weight than the heaviest single-wheeler of the time. Not without reason the change in size has often been considered to date from the Caledonian Dunalastair I class of 4-4-0 in 1896, and those engines can form a good starting point for Chapter 10.

# 10 The Years 1896-1922

By the time the first Dunalastair 4-4-0s were completed at St Rollox works in January 1896 at a cost of £2150 apiece a general increase in locomotive size was incipient due to the introduction of the first few vestibuled trains of heavier stock, beginning in 1893 with new 10-car sets for what became the well-known 2.0 pm Corridor between Euston and Glasgow, and because of the spread of steam train heating. Many more dining and sleeping cars were put on in the late 1890s along with heavier corridor ordinary coaches. Train speeds also tended to increase except on the Anglo-Scottish services, the East and West Coast schedules of which after 1896 were stabilised by agreement at 8/8¼hr and were not accelerated until 1932. Higher commercial speeds and heavier loads became more than a prospect as continuous brakes of Westinghouse and vacuum types were further developed, for traction was not the only problem. Increase in locomotive size to cope with new requirements could be taken by the 90 and 100lb steel rails being laid on more main lines. All these things brought a quick end to the single-driver as effective motive power.

The 27 years from 1896 to the 1923 Grouping were characterised not just by increased size but by greater complexity of steam reciprocating locomotives and by the first trials of other types such as the steam turbine and Paget's eight-cylinder single-acting sleeve-valve locomotive. Multi-cylinder propulsion with single-expansion came to be regarded as normal. Very large tank engines were

*Dunalastair,* first of the well-known Caledonian class that began the big-boiler high-output era on British railways in 1896. (Museum of British Transport)

developed for fast passenger trains and for heavy short-distance mineral haulage. Weights of the heaviest locomotives, maximum evaporative surface and maximum drawbar horsepower all rose by about 85 per cent within that period, and turntable diameter at main sheds went up by 30 per cent to 65ft.

Superheating was one of the two principal technical advances made in those 27 years and was the penultimate major advance in British steam locomotive practice. Within the 16 years 1906-23 high-temperature superheating extended from a single prototype to nearly 5000 applications. Second technical progressive measure was the general adoption of Walschaerts valve motion, at first in multi-cylinder locomotives and from 1913 (on the GNR and LSWR) in two-cylinder engines. To this period belong also the only two British two-cylinder 4-4-0s with outside cylinders and outside valve motion (*Snaigow* and *Durn* on the Highland in 1916).

Multi-cylinder single-expansion propulsion began in 1897 with over-cylindered machines as recorded in the previous chapter, and though the uncoupling of the Drummond 4-2-2-0s was not repeated those engines lasted in that form until Grouping days; and over-cylindering or under-boilering was a feature of several of the multi-cylinder 4-6-0s that followed. Early multi-cylinder engines had slide valves, and the reduction in cylinder diameter eased the total pressure on the backs of the slide valves, which with 20in cylinders and 180 to 200psi was becoming excessive in two-cylinder engines. In fact this load on the valve back was a reason why some engineers felt a thorough examination of long-travel valve possibilities was unwarranted. Efforts to reduce the

First LNWR superheated 4-4-0 the George V class of 1911. The class formed the most reliable and hardest-worked passenger power of the LNWR in its last 12 years.

load on D-valves usually brought tortuous passages to and from the cylinders and impeded steam and exhaust flow.

With the coming of superheating the piston valve replaced the flat-D valve, usually because of lubrication difficulties; and then in time, as desired outputs rose, the piston valve itself became a critical constituent, not in friction-producing pressure but because room was hard to find for valves big enough to suit inside cylinders of 20-21in dia partly because space had to be found for bypass valves in addition, and also because of sealing difficulties.

Taken as a whole the years from 1903 to 1922 were ones of frustration and a repetition of those earlier stages when, with very few exceptions, locomotive superintendents showed themselves incapable of coping with new demands for substantial power increase without years of trouble and expense to their employers, their staffs and themselves. Few locomotives came near the potential outputs because the huge boilers, large cylinders and rising pressures were negated first by inadequate valves, motion and draughting, and secondly by serious leakage of superheated steam past the piston valves.

Dunalastair size was little above that of existing 4-4-0s, a mere 3in being added to the boiler diameter and nothing to that of the cylinders; but the engines were well proportioned in boiler and cylinder port dimensions, and had the Adams vortex blast pipe, so some balance existed between steam-generating and steam-utilising portions. Moreover the engines were worked hard and fast daily on non-stop runs of 100 to 150 miles by drivers encouraged to be enthusiastic and competent, and the locomotive proportions enabled this to be done without inordinate fuel consumption. This standard of daily performance was the factor that really began the new era.

For two or three years thereafter no great increase was made in locomotive size on any railway; that came only with the first 10-wheelers – the GNR and LYR Atlantics of 1898-9 and the two NER 4-6-0 classes in 1899-1900. Two of the concurrent 4-4-0s, the Claud Hamiltons on the GER and the NER class R, were more competent express locomotives than any of those 10-wheelers. The first GWR 4-6-0s, Nos 36 of 1896 and 2601 of 1899, are not considered here, for they were short-lived double-frame freight engines outside the stream of development. The Highland Castle class, appearing first in 1900, had only 5ft 9in wheels and was specifically for the long Grampian grades.

On an adhesion weight of $33\frac{1}{2}$ to 35 tons the Claud Hamiltons handled 350/400-ton trains on 49mph schedules over non-stop runs up to 130 miles with ruling grades of 1 in 70 and 1 in 95-100. In their heyday, fortunately, they were oil burners, for coal firing rate on these duties would have promoted

*Claud Hamilton,* GER oil-burning 4-4-0 of 1900 which handled daily eight times the locomotive weight on the 49mph schedule of the Norfolk Coast Express.

short firebox and tube life and more lineside fires. When turned over to solid fuel around 1910 hand-picked coal was stowed on the tenders, but by that time 4-6-0s to supplant them on the hardest turns were on the drawing board and appeared in 1912.

Of slightly greater size and weight though with the same grate area, the 52-ton NER R-class 4-4-0s were quite the equals of the first 72-ton two-cylinder Atlantics and continued on the first-flight Anglo-Scottish and other express workings with trains up to 300 tons until 1910-11. They had Smith's segmental-ring piston valves below the cylinders, and as the NER preferred direct drive without rocking shafts the valves were inclined up at 1 in 31 and the cylinders themselves were inclined down at 1 in 11.

Atbara and City classes on the GWR and the Midland compounds were 4-4-0s apart. The GWR types retained double frames and four-bearing crank axles, and the Cities were the first engines to have Churchward taper boilers. They were good runners with many high end-to-end average speeds to their credit and an ability to run freely at 80-85mph down slight grades, but not at the 102.3mph claimed for so long for *City of Truro* on 9 May 1904 with the Ocean Mail special from Plymouth – a figure probably a dozen miles an hour

higher than the actual. The Midland compounds began as powerful advanced engines, but the owning railway never built anything bigger.

A steady increase in 4-4-0 size continued from 1880 to 1912, but for the dimensions the big 4-4-0s of 1903-23 were disappointing, for they could never develop a drawbar horsepower at speed at all commensurate with their boiler size (NER class R1, GCR Directors, LSWR Drummond 463 class, SECR class L) or could do so only on extravagant coal consumption (LNWR Precursor and George V classes). Yet adhesion weights reached 42 tons, boiler pressure 225psi, grate areas 27sq ft, and heating surfaces 1740sq ft. Many 4-4-0s of 1903-10 appeared first with saturated steam but later revisions or rebuilds were superheated. All except the GWR Counties were ruined by limited valve arrangements and congested front ends despite the wide use (not confined to 4-4-0s) of variable blast pipes such as the Adams vortex. Macallan top-cap, Churchward jumper top, NER sliding type, Whitelegg coned type linked to the reversing gear, and the Jones 'back hole' pattern. Superheating and piston valves of themselves made no difference to these aspects.

Fuel economy was not of prime importance when coal was well under £1 a ton. Though the line had to be drawn before the coal-eating propensities of the GSWR Drummond saturated-steam 58-ton 0-6-0s of 1913 (80 to 90lb/mile and at times 100lb) and something not far short in the corresponding saturated-steam 4-4-0s, there was still truth in the old adage 'one first class passenger pays the coal bill'. Nevertheless, the hard work engendered by heavier and faster trains headed by locomotives of great internal resistance led to steam production at uneconomic firing rates, to much wear and tear, and to line disruption by failures. Over the years 1912-14, for example, the LNWR, with about 2450 locomotives actually at work each day, suffered 125 to 155 locomotive casualties in service every month, of which 18 to 20 per cent were tube failures.

Just as almost all the eight-wheel 4-4-0s of 1871-7 that began the big step from six-wheelers were ineffective, so the 4-4-2s and 4-6-0s of 1898-1901 did not justify by the their performance the more expensive construction and heavier weight. The successful big era really began with the GNR large-boiler Atlantic No 251 in December 1902, yet even so the potentialities were approached only after superheaters were applied from 1910 and the design was unbalanced in that neither potential cylinder power nor tractive effort measured up in any way to the boiler. Benefits from balanced slide valves with exhaust direct through the back to the blast pipe

First really big-boilered British engine was the Ivatt 251 class 4-4-2, built to a total of 91 two-cylinder simples and two four-cylinder compounds from 1902 to 1910. (W. J. Reynolds)

were invalidated by short travel and short lap, and though the performance was above that of the small-boiler Atlantics and the rough and ineffective Ivatt 4-4-0s many years elasped before it reached acceptable standards.[53]

These engines were followed by Atlantic classes on the NER, GCR and GWR (1903), on the NBR and LBSCR (1906) at weights ranging up to 75 tons. The last-named were copies of the GNR design; otherwise all had deep narrow fireboxes of 26-27sq ft of grate area. The GWR began with a de Glehn four-cylinder compound from France, went to a two-cylinder simple No 171 in 1904 and 13 more in 1905 plus two larger French compounds the same year, and came to the one four-cylinder simple 4-4-2 *North Star* in 1906. Thereafter Atlantic development on the GWR ceased, and apart from the three French engines all 4-4-2s were converted to 4-6-0s by January 1913. Of the other 'Atlantic lines' only the NER developed further designs, in two-cylinder, four-cylinder compound and, from 1911, three-cylinder forms.

From 1906 to 1924 Atlantic haulage was normal all the way from King's Cross to Aberdeen. Taken together the Atlantics of the East Coast partners were representative of that completely independent non-scientific attitude to a common problem that in British locomotive practice probably reached its peak over the years 1904-14. The GNR big-boiler

Churchward's epoch-making Star 4-6-0s on the GWR were built in six classes between 1907 and 1914. With the Queens of 1910-11 superheaters were fitted new.

class had wide fireboxes, small inadequate cylinders, balanced flat slide valves, crude details, somewhat rough construction (the 'Doncaster sixteenth' was proverbial), and were anything but smooth riders. The NER class Z three-cylinder machines had deep round-top narrow fireboxes of 185cu ft volume, congested motion and piston valves, 5 tons unsprung weight on the main driving wheel pair, were built like a watch, and rode beautifully. The NBR had Belpaire narrow fireboxes, two huge outside cylinders, piston valves, poor suspension, overbalance of reciprocating parts, and were such atrocious riders that the NBR board got outside opinions on their suitability. All had 80-82in wheels; piston stroke was 24in on the GNR, 26in on the NER, and 28in on the NBR. The respective cylinder volumes were in the ratio of 1.00, 1.36, and 1.34, and the heating surface ratios were 1.0, 0.945 and 0.915.

From the NER 4-6-0s with 6ft 1in and 6ft 8in wheels of 1899-1900 that wheel arrangement developed rapidly with outside and inside cylinders, often notably on low or medium axle loads, for while Atlantic axles carried up to 20 tons from 1903 no 4-6-0 got to that value before 1908 and even then it was not admitted. The first inside-cylinder 4-6-0s were the light small-wheel Oban Bogies of the Caledonian in 1902, but most striking in appearance and performance of light 4-6-0s were the 1500-class engines of the GER (1911-12) with a maximum axle load of 15.7 tons, an adhesion weight of 43.5 tons and a locomotive weight of 63 tons, which took the 400-ton Hook Continental over the 69 miles from London to Parkeston Quay in 82 min, ascending the 1 in 90-100 of Brentwood bank without falling below 32-33 mph, and with 320 tons trailing recording a minimum of 45mph, equal to a short-time output of around 1100dbhp, or 1500rhp.

In 1902 appeared the first of the 'modern' GWR 4-6-0s, No 100, and also the first GSWR engine of that axle layout. In 1903 appeared the first GCR and large-wheel Caledonian 4-6-0s and the first on the LNWR, but the last-named was a four-cylinder Webb compound goods engine with 5ft wheels. In 1905 came the LNWR two-cylinder single-expansion Experiments with 6ft 3in wheels; in 1907 the first GWR four-cylinder 4-6-0s and the Drummond four-cylinder simples on the LSWR; in 1908 the LYR four-cylinder simples; and in 1913 the LNWR Claughtons of the same type. All cylinders in the last-named class drove the first coupled axle; all the other four-cylinder models had the drive divided between first and second axles. The LYR type of 1908 was the last new English 4-6-0 design with saturated steam, but in Scotland non-superheated 4-6-0s (Highland Castle class) were built until 1917.

Big two-cylinder 4-6-0s never quite seemed to reach the mark, for example the Caledonian *Cardean* and GCR Sam Fays, both with inside cylinders. On the LSWR when Urie in a fit of revulsion from Drummond's curious multi-cylinder practices went to two 22in by 28in outside cylinders he spoiled the potentialities by short-lap short-travel valves and a poor front end. However no more

Biggest engines ever owned by the LNWR were the erratic four-cylinder Claughton 4-6-0s from 1913. One is shown here at the head of an Eastbourne-Merseyside express at Stafford. (Locomotive & General Railway Photographs)

success attended multi-cylinder designs like the LYR engines of 1908, the Claughtons of 1913, and the GCR Lord Faringdons of 1920. Several designers such as Drummond, McIntosh, Robinson and Worsdell who had produced excellent 4-4-0s were not able to rise to the new techniques needed for the much bigger machines.

The GWR engines were a class apart. Not the slightest exaggeration is incurred in stating that from 1907 to 1927 the four-cylinder 4-6-0s of that line were streets ahead of any other British express engine. No other type before 1922, whatever its coal consumption, could consistently haul 450-475 tons along the level for 15 to 20min on end at a steady 60mph, as achieved by the GWR Star-class even with saturated steam. When superheated the engines did the same duty on less coal and water. Brief trials in 1910 between the GWR *Polar Star* and the LNWR Experiment 4-6-0 *Worcestershire* showed such an outstanding difference that Crewe planned the four-cylinder 4-6-0 Claughtons but neglected every one of the features that contributed to the Star's outstanding performance, and so the biggest LNWR locomotive ever was erratic in performance, and continued unabated the coal-eating features of the existing LNWR single-expansion engines.

Churchward attained his results by a careful ex-

amination of all basic factors and a review of all details of valves, valve motions and boilers. As related in Chapter 7 he applied superheating at a rate far outstripping that of all other British railways put together though he did not use such a high final temperature as most other lines. His top feed, applied more or less concurrently with superheating from 1911, he considered more as a small feedwater heater; it was an idea he got from Vaughan Pendred, editor of *The Engineer*.

With the GWR standard programme originated over the years 1904-6 had come, as a result of observing the three French compounds, a boiler pressure of 225psi for the largest types, 25psi above the highest then in use and 45psi above the general average, though the Midland had adopted 220psi for a few compounds. The GWR engines were designed intentionally to run economically in normal service at short cut-offs and for this reason a high pressure was allied to cylinders of moderate bore. Desire for greater power led some railways to go occasionally to pressures above their normal but only 'paper power' was gained, for the GWR valve and valve action lesson had not been absorbed and the engines could not be linked up to take advantage of the higher pressure.

Around 1903 Churchward set out to design a series of standard classes with many common parts

Fig 20
Culmination of Churchward's own two-cylinder 4-6-0s was the Court class of 1911-13. The first 10 had $18\frac{1}{8}$in by 30in cylinders and the last 15 had $18\frac{1}{2}$in bore

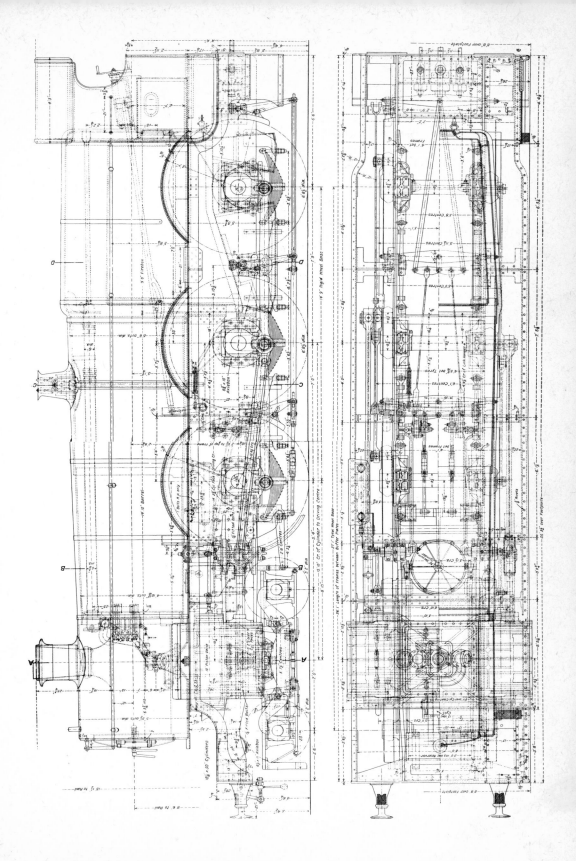

91

that would fill requirements for the 20 years until he reached retiring age. To do this the most advanced design had to be adopted; he provided this, and by 1907 all the types in the standard range had been built in the prototype batches. To make the whole idea practical the parts had to be interchangeable, but in Churchward's time this was never accomplished, particularly with boilers. The No 1 standard boiler fitted to the four-cylinder 4-6-0s and two-cylinder 4-6-0s and 2-8-0s often needed a considerable amount of small adjustment and re-fitting before it could be put on to another engine. Collett realised this, but his term as works manager from 1912 to 1919 was largely through the war years and he was able to make only small improvements. After he succeeded Churchward as chief he began at once to reorganise boiler and erecting shop procedure to get stricter interchangeability and accuracy. Only then did Churchward's 'standardisation programme' come to fruition.

Though at one time Churchward seems to have been questioned by his directors as to the supposed high cost of his four-cylinder 4-6-0s he could justly reply that they were not costly in relation to the work they did. They were not costly even without that qualification when compared with other railway-built main-line engines for which costing practice was similar. Swindon-built four-cylinder Stars were costed at £3022 to £3314 over the years 1907-14 and the two-cylinder Saints and Courts at £2530 to £2726. The Darlington-built three-cylinder 4-4-2s of the NER of 1913-14 were charged at just over £4000 apiece; those of the same design built by the North British Locomotive Co in 1911 cost £4485 each. In 1911 the saturated-steam big-boiler Atlantics of the GNR were valued at £3260 each and superheated version was shown at £3449. GER two-cylinder 4-6-0s of the 1500-class were turned out of Stratford in 1911-12 at £4000 apiece and the last-built (1910) 4-4-0s at £3550. Tenders are included in all prices. Thus the GWR 4-6-0 prices from 1907 to 1914 were £33 to £35.5/ton of empty engine and tender weight; the GNR Atlantic prices were £39.5 to £41.5, the GER types from Stratford above £50/ton, and Caledonian superheater 4-4-0s from St Rollox in 1913 about £35/ton.

Prices rocketed during 1914-19 and went higher again temporarily in 1921, and even such lightweight 4-6-0s as the Highland Clans cost £9150 apiece in 1919 with steel fireboxes, which were cheaper than copper. The war years slowed down passenger engine development, and the only new 4-6-0s for such duties were the Caledonian 60-class (1915), the LSWR 736-class (1918), and Highland Clans, all with outside cylinders and the last two with outside Walschaerts motion. The LSWR

engines had the largest high-pressure cylinders (22in by 28in) ever used in this country, but the piston thrust of 30.6 tons was equalled by that of the GSWR 4-6-4T (1922) and surpassed in LNER 4-6-2 *Enterprise* (30.8 tons) in 1928, by the Merchant Navy Pacifics at 31.7 tons, and by the BR Britannia Pacifics and the class 9 2-10-0s at 35 tons; but these were as nothing compared with the 130 to 140 tons found in North America in the 1930s.

In the years immediately following the war resuscitation of express engine building was confined to pre-war and war-time designs except for the unsuccessful Caledonian three-cylinder 4-6-0s, the successful SECR superheated 4-4-0 rebuilds, the poor Lord Faringdon 4-6-0s on the GCR, the disappointing GSWR large 4-6-4Ts, and finally the two GNR Pacifics of 1922. The last-named can be considered more conveniently in the next chapter.

The comparatively rapid up-surge in size and power over the years 1898-1904 was paralleled in tank engine construction through the years 1904-14. Early examples for normal service were the GWR 4-4-2T and 2-6-2T that were part of the planned programme, and the LNWR 4-4-2T Precursor Tanks of 1906. All these scaled around 75 tons whereas previous tanks had not got above the 68 tons of the Tilbury 51-class. From 1910 further increments in size were made with the 86-ton LBSCR 4-6-2T and in 1912-14 with the 95-ton Tilbury 4-6-4T and the 99-ton Billinton LBSCR 4-6-4T. The LBSCR weight was exceeded only nominally in later years by the GSWR and LYR/LMSR 4-6-4T of 1922-4 at 100 tons, the former having the same cylinder size as the Brighton Baltics at 22in by 26in, and the latter the four 16½in by 26in pattern as in the Hughes 4-6-0 tender engines. Other large tanks of the 1920-2 period were the 96-ton 4-6-2T and 4-8-0T on the LSWR with 21in by 28in and 22in by 28in cylinders respectively. The only 4-6-4Ts with inside cylinders were the five on the Furness Railway in 1920.

Apart from the GER experimental 0-10-0T of 1903 mentioned later, the most remarkable tank of pre-Grouping days was the North Staffordshire four-cylinder 57-ton 0-6-0T with cranks at 135° and a 50 per cent maximum cut-off in a deliberate attempt to get the highest possible accelerative power for NSR frequent-stop passenger trains. Completed in 1922 its potentialities were almost immediately swallowed up and lost in the LMS, and by 1924 the engine had been converted to tender type. It was the first engine in Britain to have four sets of Walschaerts motion, but not the first to have four independent sets of valve gear.

Another feature of the years 1897-1922 was the development of powerful mixed-traffic engines. Previously a few express goods classes had been known, such as the GER 2-6-0s of 1878 and a few large-wheel 0-6-0s; but a new line was set in 1903 with Webb's last class, the four-cylinder compound 5ft wheel 4-6-0s. His successor, Whale, perpetuated the idea but not the mechanism in his 5ft 3in inside-cylinder single-expansion Experiment-Goods in 1906.

The NER class S 4-6-0s of 1899 with 6ft wheels were said to be for passenger work, but after the first couple of years were confined largely to freight trains, and in 1911 the design was developed into a larger-boilered and more powerful S2 class that formed the backbone of NER express goods and mixed-traffic power until 1920, when it was supplemented by the even larger three-cylinder class S3 4-6-0s. One of the S2 class in 1913 was given uniflow cylinders, piston valves and Walschaerts motion and had a record for bursting cylinder covers. The three-cylinder uniflow Atlantic No 2212 of 1918 was much better.

Other railways that built small-wheel 4-6-0s included the LSWR, GCR and Caledonian, and in 1917-18 the Highland received the first of the 'Inverness Goods' with 5ft 3in wheels; but the mixed-traffic idea had various stages, as from the production of the first GWR 5ft 8in 2-6-0 in 1910

(an addition to the planned programme) several attempts were made on this wheel arrangement to evolve much freer-running types of high load capacity that would be real mixed-traffic performers (GWR, LBSCR, SECR) and not rather sluggish fish-train haulers (Caledonian and GSWR). 'Fast goods' in those days were still largely unbraked, so were limited in practice to 35mph top speed.

The Caledonian and GSWR did little more than add a short-arm pony truck to the standard 0-6-0s, and in general idea followed more the original GWR 4ft 7in wheel Aberdare coal 2-6-0s of 1901, though these had outside frames. A pony truck on the GSWR engines was essential as the basic 0-6-0 already was not far short of 60 tons and a superheater was added; nevertheless the increase in weight of the Mogul over the 0-6-0 was only $4\frac{1}{2}$ tons. The SECR 2-6-0 was the forerunner of the two-cylinder and three-cylinder SR Moguls and of the government Woolwich construction.

Under Gresley an entirely new two-cylinder 2-6-0 with outside Walschaerts motion was evolved in 1912 on the GNR, and was built in three progressive sizes culminating in the three-cylinder 1000-class in 1920, the first British locomotives to have a 6ft parallel boiler barrel and the first six-coupled tender engine other than *Great Bear* to have 60 tons of adhesion weight admitted. It was also the first Gresley class to have the conjugating levers of the valve gear in front of the valve chests. The preceding three-cylinder 2-8-0 coal engine had

GNR Mogul of 1920 with parallel 6ft boiler and a single-ring barrel. First engine to have the front lever arrangement of Gresley's conjugated valve motion. Forerunner of LNER class K3. (W. J. Reynolds)

the conjugating levers behind the cylinders; and in view of Gresley's later temporary practice with the Pacifics it is noteworthy that both these types had $5\frac{1}{2}$in max valve travel, $1\frac{1}{4}$in lap and $\frac{1}{8}$in lead. The two-cylinder 2-6-0s handled much war-time passenger traffic, and from the beginning the three-cylinder Moguls were almost equally engaged in passenger and freight work and could well be regarded as originating the powerful general-purpose engine as that term was understood through the later Group and BR periods.

Concurrent with the passenger and mixed-traffic engine progressions was an enhancement of freight power, mainly by the construction of eight-coupled engines in place of 0-6-0s, but with a few big-boiler specimens of the latter such as NER classes P2 and P3 with 5ft 6in barrels and around 50 tons of weight.

Apart from two locomotives on the Taff Vale, eight-coupled tender engines began with one Webb single-expansion 0-8-0 in 1892 and a series of similar three-cylinder compounds from 1893, followed by four-cylinder compounds 1901-3. Not until 1900-3 did other lines adopt 0-8-0s and then with two single-expansion cylinders. but whereas the GNR, Caledonian and LYR favoured inside cylinders driving the second axle the NER and GCR preferred outside cylinders driving the third axle through long rods. All lay within a weight range of 53-58 tons, but over the next 15 years larger-boiler machines scaling up to 66 tons were developed, particularly on the NER, which later still, in 1920, went to a three-cylinder 0-8-0 of 72 tons weight, but here the drive was concentrated on the second axle. The Caledonian engines (1901) were the only British 0-8-0s to have the logical spacing of the wheels, the second and third pairs being close together and the end pairs far apart to give adequate length for connecting rods at the front and ample firebox length at the back. The same principle was applied at the forward end of Caledonian 0-8-0Ts (1903).

Engines of 2-8-0 layout were nearly as numerous as 0-8-0s but were not so widespread. After Webb's retirement many of his compound 0-8-0s were rebuilt as 2-8-0s. The GWR 2-8-0 was one of the first of the planned standards and was introduced in 1903. By 1914 two-cylinder 2-8-0s were running also on the GNR, GCR and Somerset & Dorset, but the LNWR went back to 0-8-0s with two inside cylinders, a layout adopted by the Hull & Barnsley in 1907.

GCR 0-8-0s originating in 1902 were developed in 1911 into a 2-8-0 with the same wheels, tyres, axleboxes, motion details, etc. A leading pony truck was incorporated to assist in taking the weight of a bigger and superheated boiler and larger cylinders

with piston valves; boilers were duplicates of those on the GCR Atlantics. By the beginning of World War I the GCR had 126 of these 2-8-0s, and the design was adopted with only one major change (a steel firebox) as the Ministry of Munitions standard for heavy freight haulage overseas in what became known as the ROD type, of which 521 were built to government orders by seven works in 1917-19. After the war they were hired out to many railways in this country, and then sold outright to the GWR, LNER and LMS over several years.

These engines were never cheap in first cost despite their general simplicity. GCR engines built in Glasgow in 1912 cost £4500 per engine and tender on deferred payments spread over five years, at a time when Swindon was building GWR standard Consolidations for £2950 to £3000 and the NER was turning out of Darlington 66-ton 0-8-0s at £2975. With wartime rises the ROD engines cost from £6030 in 1917 to nearly £10,000 in 1919; but as secondhand sales they reached an all-time low, for the last 75 were sold from dumps to the LMS in 1927 at £340 per engine and tender.

The GWR 2-8-0s had the No 1 boiler as used in the 4-6-0s and the 18in by 30in cylinders of the two-cylinder 4-6-0s, though in the 2-8-0s the cylinders were set horizontally $2\frac{1}{2}$in above axle centre line to keep the necessary clearance for the truck wheels without inclining the drive line. They formed a considerable advance in GWR main-line freight power, particularly on the South Wales to London coal trains, which despite a 125-mile haul and the existence of a number of the Aberdare 2-6-0s had previously been hauled much by pairs of 0-6-0Ts.

Two major railways, the Midland and the NBR, never got above 0-6-0s, of 50 tons weight on the former and 55 tons on the latter. Biggest 0-6-0s were the GER 1270-class of 1920 with boiler and 20in by 28in cylinders standard with those in the express 4-6-0s. Low unit bridge loading on the GER meant a long wheelbase for any heavy engine and these 0-6-0s were spread over 18ft 10in, giving a linear loading of no more than 2.91 tons/ft run. Maximum permissible axle load on GER main lines had risen to 18.75 tons from the 17.5 tons in 1910-12.

These GER engines had 4ft 11in wheels; the usual run for an 0-6-0 was between 4ft 6in for mineral types and 5ft 3in for general freight services, but a few larger-wheel engines formed an interesting diversion. As with several other locomotive matters they began with John Gray on the Hull & Selby with two engines in 1844 having 5ft 6in wheels. McConnell used the same diameter for over a hundred of the Wolverton Goods between 1853 and 1863. On the NER a few otherwise standard 0-6-0s were given 5ft 8in wheels in 1880-2 and two in 1883 had 5ft 6in, and some lasted into LNER days. Deeley converted three of the Johnson 5ft 3in 0-6-0s to 6ft wheels in 1906, the largest diameter recorded in a British 0-6-0. Major application was on the GNR with 15 saturated-steam engines with 5ft 8in wheels in 1908 and another 10 with superheaters in 1912.

A diameter of 5ft 3in was no bar to speed, and in LMS days the Fowler 0-6-0s ran frequently at 55 to 60mph on excursion and secondary passenger trains, and in earlier years the Webb Cauliflower and rebuilt DX engines with 5ft wheels galloped along at 70-72mph when piloting main-line expresses, which meant 390rpm or $6\frac{1}{2}$revs/sec.

Increasing mineral traffic still largely handled in 8-ton and 10-ton wagons, plus a larger number of slow-speed unbraked and pick-up freights, began to obtrude uncomfortably on operating departments and their boards of directors in the early years of this century. On the Midland a completely new traffic-control scheme had to be inaugurated in 1907, for the South Yorkshire and Derbyshire coal-train congestion was so great and means of dispersing it so ineffective that locomotive crews were known to mount their engine and leave it again after an eight-hour shift without having turned a wheel. This was not the fault of the locomotive superintendent, but the new Midland scheme took 'running' away from him and put it under the operating superintendent, a system perpetuated on the LMS and BR.

Reorganisation of freight traffic led on several lines to large marshalling yards at strategic points, with humps between the reception roads and sorting sidings. The high necessary tractive or pushing effort to get heavy trains over the humps brought some notable special tank engines that in their working hours reached a speed above 10mph only for a few hundred yards when running light to take up another train. Examples were the Caledonian 0-8-0T (1903), the 84-ton LYR 0-8-2T (1908), the LNWR 0-8-2T (1911) that also dealt with short-haul mineral trains in South Wales, as did the GWR 2-8-0T class, and in 1920 the LSWR 4-8-0T for Feltham yard. In the last years of the LNWR the 0-8-2T was developed into an 88-ton 0-8-4T that was used also for banking and local coal haulage. All these were two-cylinder types, with inside cylinders and motion on the Caledonian, LYR and LNWR, outside cylinders and inside motion on the GWR, and outside cylinders with outside motion on the LSWR.

First of all such engines, however, were the $96\frac{1}{2}$-ton GCR 0-8-4Ts dating from 1907 for Wath yard near Barnsley; they were followed in 1909 by a 4-8-0T class on the NER for the then new Erimus yard on Teesside. Both types were given three 18in by 26in cylinders, 55/56in wheels and 180psi pressure to get ample pushing power and even torque, and had 74 and 67 tons of adhesion respectively.

In contrast to all other NER three-cylinder locomotives (4-4-2, 4-6-0, 0-8-0, 4-4-4T, 4-6-2T) the drive of the 4-8-0T was divided over two axles, but access to the six eccentrics and inside drive was restricted by a low pitched boiler and long side tanks that had a 5in cross equalising pipe above the motion. The GCR tank showed yet further complication and lack of access arising from multi-cylinder propulsion with divided drive on a tank locomotive, and was worse, because of the tanks and a large boiler blow-off cock than the NER three-cylinder class Z Atlantics with six eccentrics and one crank throw with a strap-type big end on the forward coupled axle.

First of all 20th Century three-cylinder engines was the remarkable 0-10-0T of the GER completed in December 1902 and which did nothing more than a few carefully-measured trial trips in 1903. It was remarkable for its naïveté or for its sublety according to whether one holds the view that James Holden and his designer F. V. Russell were serious and simply magnified in their own minds the various problems as they came up, or were treating the whole idea of getting 300 tons of moving weight from standstill to 30mph in 30sec as a joke. Holden was a serious-minded Quaker then 65 years of age and went to the expense of a patent for certain features, so a light-hearted approach was not likely.

This 80-ton engine[56] was full of bizarrities, if such an expression can be accepted, including an axle with a single-throw crank that took no drive line; an open-work inside connecting rod that encircled the 'cranked straight' axle in front of it to obviate the use of an inclined inside cylinder; three blower rings; six $3\frac{1}{2}$in safety valves; automatic sanding tied in to the regulator mechanism; and a curved sliding door at the back of the cab to ease fire-iron manipulation. The boiler was the largest used in Britain up to that time, the barrel being 5ft $4\frac{1}{4}$in dia and 15ft 11in between tubeplates with a wide firebox 7ft $9\frac{1}{2}$in across the foundation ring and a grate area of 42sq ft. The barrel contained 395 tubes $1\frac{3}{4}$in od, but the smokebox that went with this huge ensemble was under 3ft long and had a volume of no more than 100 cu ft gross and 82cu ft net.

One more 10-coupled engine was built in the period 1896-1922 and also had abnormal features. This was the Midland four-cylinder 0-10-0 tender engine known generally as Big Bertha, built at Derby for banking on the Lickey incline and on which it operated until after nationalisation. It was full of Midland eccentricities and poor practices, magnified by two cross-ported piston valves for the four cylinders. Operating only over a four-mile section without horizontal curves the wheelbase of 20ft 11in was no trouble in service, though the vertical curve where the 1 in 37 ended was not entirely to its liking.

If diversity, complexity and occasional abnormality were prominent in the period under consideration, standardisation of parts also made some headway. This had been practised widely at Crewe from 1859-60 and from the 1870s spare standard boilers were kept in hand to reduce the time an engine was out of traffic for repairs. Boilers standard among 2-2-2, 2-4-0 and 0-4-2 classes were not uncommon even on such small railways as the Edinburgh & Glasgow from around 1860, and components standard among two or three classes were found in Stirling's time on the GNR and Holden's on the GER, but always with the current limitations of manufacturing accuracy, A higher degree of accuracy allied to a rigid standardisation of parts was one of the firm bases on which Aspinall established the new Horwich works of the LYR in 1888-9.

Though only on the GWR was a complete programme for half a dozen different classes drawn up at one time, a comprehensive system of parts standardisation was a major feature of GCR locomotive practice under Robinson from 1902, on the LSWR under Urie from 1912, and to a lesser extent on other lines. With the continuous advance in machine tool equipment and shop procedures the approach to complete interchangeability became closer though no railway seems to have introduced anything approaching a real limits-and-fits policy, and thus much remained to be done by the Group railways.

New construction over the last three years before Grouping was overshadowed by the Railways Act (1921) and comprised a strange mixture of progressive types (GNR 2-6-0, 2-8-0, 4-6-2 and GWR 5ft 8in wheel 2-8-0), old methods taken up to the limits (NER three-cylinder 4-6-2, 4-6-0, 0-8-0 and LSWR 4-6-0), sheer costive designs with long antecedents (LYR four-cylinder 4-6-0, Caledonian Pickersgill 4-4-0, Midland 0-6-0), and a few oddities. Had Grouping not come, British steam locomotive design might well have remained at 1914 levels, for no more notice would have been taken of the bright exceptions than had been accorded the fundamental advances of progressive engineers in earlier years.

# 11   The Group Era

Under the Railways Act (1921) 123 different undertakings, not all operators, were brought together into four big systems known generally as the Group railways, which began as such on 1 January 1923 and ceased to exist on 31 December 1947. A few narrow-gauge and other railways were not brought into the Groups and a few joint lines remained joint among two Groups. Of these the most important owning locomotives were the Somerset & Dorset and the Midland & Great Northern Joint.

Approximately 23,880 standard-gauge steam locomotives of about 36 different wheel arrangements passed into Group ownership, and another 350 or so remained with the joint lines and smaller undertakings. The approximate division was: London Midland & Scottish (LMS) 10,316 of which about 3200 were tank engines and the remainder tender types; London & North Eastern (LNER) 4863 tender and 2520 tank; Great Western (GWR) 1486 tender and 2415 tank; Southern (SR) 1182 tender and 1099 tank. The LMS total was in 393 classes and sub-classes, the LNER total in 236, and the SR total in 139.

As the railways were to be Grouped as a national measure, much could have been done to ensure that they began on a proper footing, as for six years the railways had been under government control, the stock and track had deteriorated greatly through war conditions, the labour situation had become chaotic, and the financial groundwork had gone to seed in much the same proportion as the national debt, which had increased from £700 million in 1914 to £7000 million in 1919. But under the 1921 Act the railways were simply told to Group themselves by 1923 and thereafter were thrown back on their own depleted resources.

Failure to provide the ground on which Grouping could thrive as a national asset was reflected as far as locomotive stock and line operation were concerned in three great missed opportunities: (1) no directions or guidance were given as to the appositeness of national standard locomotive types, though by the Act the Minister of Transport had power to require the gradual standardisation of equipment; (2) the structure gauge remained unaltered; (3) a policy of fitting nearly all freight stock with continuous brakes was neglected.

Towards the end of the war, working under the direction of the Railway Executive Committee, the Association of Railway Locomotive Engineers had begun to draw up designs for standard 2-6-0 and 2-8-0 types. This work was shelved as soon as peace broke out, but the SECR 2-6-0, which had been the

basis for a proposed standard Mogul, was approved for a number of engines ordered to be built at Woolwich Arsenal to relieve unemployment. That the principle itself was not unfeasible was shown after Grouping when engines were transferred from one end of the new systems to the other and almost at once showed how erroneous was the belief that every railway had locomotives best suited to its own conditions.

In existence in 1920 were 66 different loading gauges applicable to 150 sections of line, and of all the railways grouped only 18 could take anything like the largest outlines. The structure gauges that fixed loading limits were governed by comparatively few structures, and of these the most important were small tunnels; the great majority of platforms, buildings and bridges and many tunnels were well outside the minima. The complete structure gauge could have been enlarged to the existing maximum without any need to alter the standard six-foot between tracks; at national expense the cost probably would not have exceeded two days' war expenditure.

Similar national procedure could have been applied to the fitting of continuous brakes to nearly all wagons. A few braked freights had run from the turn of the century, but the prevalence of unbraked freight and mineral trains up to well over 1000 tons in weight continued to ruin British railway operation by perpetuating the great gap between the speeds of the fastest and slowest trains on each section, for top speed of unbraked freights could rarely rise above 30-35mph because of difficulties in stopping when only eight or 10 pairs of wheels out of 80 to 100 were braked.

The brake question affected locomotive design on several counts, for power characteristics are quite different when trains operate at top speeds of 60mph instead of 30mph; it affected locomotive stock also because more locomotives are needed to work a given traffic at slow speed, and both engines and crews have more idle time. Insistence by the new Ministry of Transport on a standard driving position on one side or the other would also have been warranted.

The railways, having been told to Group themselves but otherwise to continue the usual *laissez-faire* under their reduced circumstances, did so right well. Each Group set off and continued with locomotive designs and practices of its own that varied with successive chief mechanical engineers. There were 13 all told, who were as independent as in Edwardian days, but constrained by circumstances to move along more concentrated lines. In one respect the policy of the first four cmes was alike, in that there was little rebuilding of pre-1923 designs to more modern standards, though on the two biggest groups there was much new construction to pre-1923 and even pre-1914 designs.

After beginnings encompassed with difficulties, within a dozen years of the Grouping there arose the final stage in British steam locomotive development in a technical sense: an almost complete balance on a high standard of design, construction, operation and maintenance, and at the same time a true balance in design between steam generation, steam utilisation and vehicular portions of the locomotives themselves. No longer were locomotives under-cylindered or over-cylindered, under-boilered or over-boilered; no longer did inadequate valves and valve motions tie together the legs of potentially fast horses or divert locomotives from their function of traffic shifting to one of coal consuming. Moreover operating and locomotive departments came to work in close accord to ginger up the entire field of railway working, and so the efforts of the locomotive engineers were actually transmuted into higher commercial speeds, greater traffic capacity,

reduced cost per net ton-mile, and better service.

These results were not achieved at once. To get drivers accustomed to the part-regulator long cut-off methods needed to keep short-lap short-travel engines out of trouble to change over to full regulator and restricted cut-off was a business in itself, but nothing at all to the business of the top echelons. The initial 10-year period from 1923 to 1932 was occupied much with the boards and chief executives acquiring experience of handling large organisations; and on the mechanical engineering side the technical knowledge of 1922 was not enough to cope with new conditions that at once spotlighted its deficiences. Only two channels measured up to Group requirements or could be extrapolated easily to meet them. They were (1) the standard locomotive practice of the GWR, and (2) Gresley's work on the GNR from 1918-20.

The GWR itself got through the early years of Grouping with least trouble for in essence there was no Grouping, only the absorption of the Cambrian and several small Welsh-valley lines. Effective influence of the South Wales companies was only the indirect .one of a new GWR locomotive class, the 66XX 0-6-2T; Cambrian requirements largely led to the production of another new standard, the lightweight 2251-class 0-6-0. But the time had come most conveniently for new standards on existing principles, Churchward's planned programme had

Train of five GWR 0-6-2Ts en route to Swindon from the works of the builder, Armstrong-Whitworth, 1928.

just served its intended two decades and a new cme, with long Swindon traditions, had been in the saddle for 12 months.

Near completion of a lengthy bridge strengthening programme enabled Collett at Swindon to introduce a larger four-cylinder 4-6-0 in 1923. These Castle-class engines had an adhesion weight scarcely two tons more than that of the four-cylinder engines of 1914, but that was enough to permit a 10in lengthening at the back end and the installation of a firebox with 12 per cent more grate area and 6 per cent more heating surface. The back end of the taper barrel was only 3in bigger than that of the standard No 1 boiler and the pressure of 225psi was retained; but the cylinder volume was increased by 14 per cent.

Standard of performance was higher than Churchward had been able to attain by 1914. That engineer had set himself to get a drawbar pull of 2 tons at 70mph from his express engines; the French Atlantics were the first to give it, but by 1908 he was getting it and more from the Stars in normal service. In 1924 the Castles were measured on test to sustain 2.35 tons at 71mph, but in service thereafter they frequently exceeded that measure,

and they were probably the greatest single influence in forwarding British locomotive design through the last 40 years of new construction.

When the bridge strengthening programme was complete a further extrapolation was made in 1927 with the Kings, the most powerful 4-6-0s to run anywhere. but with the high axle load of 22½ tons they had restricted route availability and only 30 were built over a span of three years, whereas 171 Castles were constructed at Swindon over a period of 27 years. The Kings were soon handling 550-ton trains from London to Westbury, 95 miles, on mile-a-minute schedules, and took up to 375 tons unpiloted over the 1 in 40 South Devon grades. No new two-cylinder express 4-6-0s were built for the GWR between 1913 and 1945, but many mixed-traffic engines of that axle layout with 5ft 8in and 6ft wheels were turned out.

On the LNER Gresley was the obvious choice for cme. Robinson of the GCR was doyen of the old chiefs and Raven of the NER the most forceful, but both were on retiring age while Gresley, with a dozen successful years behind him as chief on the GNR, was still under 50. He was ready and able to meet the greatly increased responsibilities, and dominated his department from the beginning.

At no time did he incline to a policy of strict standardisation based on a limited number of planned classes, though parts standardisation was not

Most powerful 4-6-0s to run in any country were the GWR four-cylinder Kings, built 1927-30. (British Railways)

First Gresley three-cylinder Pacific, No 1470 of the
GNR, April 1922.

neglected. He brought out new designs as the traffic
required, and though tying himself for main-line
power to three-cylinder propulsion with conjugated
valve motion, and using a trailing carrying axle with
a wide firebox above it whenever possible, he was
not at all averse in the early stages to perpetuating
pre-Group designs of other men for specific jobs and
areas. He preferred concentrating the drive of
three-cylinder engines on the second coupled axle of
six- or eight-coupled types because he felt the front
axle had sufficient to cope with in large flange
forces. In coming to the Sandringham 4-6-0s he had
to accept divided drive.

Gresley's practice was progressive from the time
he succeeded H. A. Ivatt on the GNR; but from the
inception of his three-cylinder 2-8-0 coal engine in
1918 and the big-boiler 1000-class three-cylinder
Mogul of 1920 he moved definitely into new concep-
tions of size and power that culminated, in
pre-Grouping days, in his first two A1-class Pacifics
of 1922. In later years he was once asked why these
two engines had been successful from the start
whereas the GWR *Great Bear* of 1908 had been a
failure. He replied: 'Because I was thinking about
and scheming mine from 1914.' Yet his two Pacifics
as built were back-breakers and only moderate performers for their size. Not until the GWR valve-mo-
tion and pressure principles had been incorporated
did they become outstanding.

More as a publicity measure than as a considered
move, the general managers of the GWR and LNER
in 1925 arranged trials of a Castle 4-6-0 and a
Gresley 180lb Pacific over the lines of both com-

panies, between Paddington and Plymouth and
between King's Cross and Doncaster. The 80-ton
4-6-0 had the better of the 92-ton Pacific on almost
every count of haulage, speed and line performance
with a 10-12 per cent economy in fuel and water.
The Pacific had much the bigger boiler and the first
of the modern combustion-chamber fireboxes, but
its valve gear, valve proportions and setting
prevented steam being used efficiently, and it was
pre-eminently in this aspect that the GWR engine
scored. Yet Gresley was hard to convince, and only
in 1927 did Pacifics appear with revised valve motion. With the same 180psi boiler pressure, coal consumption on 400/450-ton Anglo-Scottish trains at
52mph averages came down from 52 to 38lb/mile,
and at once gave possibilities of longer through runs
and longer non-stop runs.

In 1928 Gresley adopted the second of the GWR
principles, high pressure, by going to 220psi, for his
valve gear could now deal with it. Any economy
from this alteration could not be judged because at
the same time 43 superheater elements were put on
in place of 32; but the new engines were much more
sprightly than the 180lb engines, and this new
pressure, or a higher one, plus the revised valve
gear, was adopted for all future main-line
locomotives — 4-6-2, 2-8-2 and 2-6-2. The 220lb
revised valve gear Pacifics could haul a 475/500-ton
passenger train along the level at a mile-a-minute
with full throttle and no more than 15 to 18 per cent
cut-off, thus equalling for the first time the standards of performance common on the GWR from
1907-10.

The increased haulage power of the 220psi
engines was necessary, for by 1930 the weight of
many main-line trains had gone up from around

400 tons at Grouping to 500 tons, not because of more vehicles in the train but because of heavier stock (with greater lighting loads) which had to be hauled non-stop over the 268 miles from London to Newcastle in place of the 188 miles to York. The Edinburgh non-stops, which brought the eight-wheel non-bogie corridor tenders, were an easy proposition until 1932 for they were to a schedule of under 50mph.

Through the authoritative personality of the new general manager, Sir Herbert Walker, the Southern Railway had a relatively easy settling down period, and Maunsell, the automatic choice as cme from the new Group's personnel, moved cautiously but steadily in his locomotive policy. He had already adopted taper boilers and some of the GWR valve motion tenets on the SECR in his initial 2-6-0 and 2-6-4T types and in the 4-4-0 rebuilds of 1920, influenced by two of his Swindon-trained assistants G. H. Pearson and H. Holcroft. His SECR 2-6-0 of 1917 was the second British locomotive to combine long-lap long-travel valves with high superheat, the

first being GWR No 2901 in 1906 (see Chapter 7).

After the first six or seven years the steam locomotive design and production side of the SR declined under increasing electrification. Maunsell's productions reflected his own characteristics of sound but not inspired engineering, common sense, and an appreciation of the proportion and fitness of things; though at the beginning he did not envisage a planned programme of standard types, his parts standardisation was thorough. Every one of these aspects was changed completely under Maunsell's successor, Bulleid, and as regards steam locomotive engineering the 25 years of the SR was cleft in two — in design, construction and administration.

Maunsell built only 10 designs entirely of his own, and though eight were regarded as Southern standards some were built in such restricted numbers that that term was hardly justified. They comprised the Lord Nelson, King Arthur, H15 (6ft wheels) and S15 (5ft 7in wheels) 4-6-0s, the Schools 4-4-0s, the N-class (5ft 6in wheels) and U-class (6ft wheels) 2-6-0s, and Z-class three-cylinder 0-8-0Ts. Also built, largely with standard parts, were the W-class three-cylinder freight 2-6-4T with 5ft 6in wheels and, in 1925, the ill-fated River-class 2-6-4Ts later rebuilt to 2-6-0 tender engines after

Three-cylinder Schools class, Southern Railway, 1930, the most powerful and effective 4-4-0s ever to run in Britain. (Museum of British Transport)

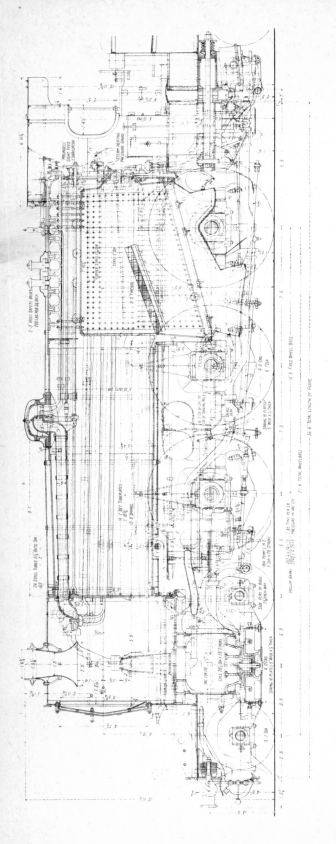

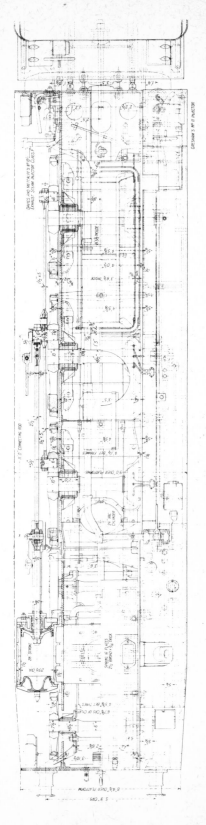

Bulleid Merchant Navy 4-6-2 at Exeter in 1945 after the first alteration to the front cowling. (W. H. C. Kelland)

several derailments culminating in the Sevenoaks disaster of 1927. One good ex-LSWR feature was retained in all Maunsell 4-6-0s and in the Schools — the 7ft 6in bogie wheelbase introduced by Adams in 1880.

First in point of time were the two-cylinder King Arthurs, the most uniformly successful and reliable six-coupled main-line engines of the SR. They were the first move to try and cope with the traffic department's requirement for an engine to haul 500 tons on 55mph schedules, and from 1926 they were supplemented by the four-cylinder 135°-crank Lord Nelson 4-6-0s, one of the first British designs in which boiler proportions were drawn up deliberately on the basis of all British, Continental and American knowledge; yet the boiler and front end layout did not always provide free steaming. Because of the selected crank arrangement a choice had to be made between four sets of Walschaerts motion and a multi-lever conjugated actuation from the outside motion; the former was selected.

The three-cylinder Schools 4-4-0 of 1930-1 embodied all the lines of thought on valves, boilers and

Fig 21
General arrangement of the two-cylinder King Arthur class 4-6-0s, probably the most reliable and effective top-class motive power of the Southern Railway, 1925

accessibility supported by Maunsell, but there was an additional 'something' about them, an almost unwitting combination of correct ratios right through, apart from one detail, that made them the most powerful and effective 4-4-0s ever to run in Britain.

Bulleid's productions lay entirely within the war years and the immediate aftermath, but that in no way led him to accept the national precepts for the time of simplicity and reliability. In his Merchant Navy and West Country Pacifics he endeavoured to solve age-old problems by unconventional and undeveloped means[57] that did not bring overall success, partly because loose administration resulted in gross over-weight in the Merchant Navy class; and the performance was so erratic and the troubles so consistent as to nullify the brilliant feats of speed and haulage given on numerous occasions.[58] The Leader engine, the last locomotive effort of the SR, showed similar methods of thought *in extremis,* and there was not the slightest chance of the design earning money for the owning company.

Not one but several Caesarean operations were needed to get the LMS and its locomotive policy and department into the light, and they extended over a decade. This was the harshest of the Groups, in which the board was much concerned with finance as finance and figures as something real in themselves, and in which ruthless fights for power among chief executives were prominent, especially in the operating and locomotive sides. There was no automatic choice for general manager or cme, and

103

the seniority of George Hughes on the newly-combined LNWR/LYR brought a quiet refined chief of mechanical engineering into a milieu that would have been more responsive to Jack Dempsey.

Main obstacle to a locomotive policy suited to a system of 7400 route miles extending from Bournemouth to Thurso was the dominance of the Midland operating department, under which locomotive running had been a sub-department since 1907. This organisation was perpetuated with Midland personnel, which insisted on retention of the Midland small-engine policy despite proposals for 4-6-2s and 2-8-2s from successive cmes, and influenced the Derby locomotive design office so that the several technical weaknesses of Midland practice enjoyed greater scope and repeatedly countered break-throughs like the Horwich Crab 2-6-0s and the 2-6-4Ts.[59] Pronounced defects included short-travel short-lap valves and small bearings. Altogether 1285 pre-Group designed engines of 4-4-0, 0-6-0 and 0-6-0T types with these poor attributes were built as selected standards.

First effective impingement on this situation was that of Sir Josiah Stamp, who after becoming president of the LMS executive in 1925 was appalled at the expenditure of the locomotive and locomotive-running departments with so little to show in the way of efficiency, economy, punctuality and general standard of service. The cost accounting and statistics he introduced enforced a change. Yet so little were his methods understood that in 1928 yet another pre-Group small passenger engine was chosen as a standard and 138 built simply because it showed low values of repair costs and coal consumption. Neither this nor the fact that many of its parts were interchangeable with those of other standard classes were of much moment when all were quite unfitted to meet the requirements of a large Group under rapidly developing conditions.

Stamp's methods of investigation led also to a revision of locomotive and crew diagramming and, where shop equipment permitted, to a revision of repair and maintenance procedures to get greater mileage from existing motive power and if possible to do the work with fewer units. This side was pushed strongly by E. J. H. Lemon during his year (1931) as cme and afterwards as a vice-president, and average daily mileage per engine actually in use rose from 94.6 in 1929 to 106.7 in 1933 and 117.9 in 1938.

The continuing unsatisfactory position of LMS main-line power with Claughton, Prince of Wales and LYR 4-6-0s and George V and Midland compound 4-4-0s blasting along at maximum but insufficient drawbar output and maximum but more than sufficient coal consumption, plus the

GWR/LNER locomotive interchange trials of 1925, led the LMS board in 1926 to borrow a GWR Castle-class 4-6-0 to work for a fortnight between Euston and Crewe and for a similar period between Crewe and Carlisle. Like *Polar Star* on the LNWR trials of 1910, *Launceston Castle* maintained so easily all the times and loads that were wearing out the LMS purse and engines that the board gave instructions for a similar locomotive to be developed and 50 built in time for the next summer's traffic. This resulted in the Royal Scots, the first big passenger engine of the LMS, and a successful one for the time. In it were mixed Swindon, Horwich and Derby practices including features from the immediately preceding 2-6-4Ts plus a dash of sound thinking from brief consultations with the SR especially in regard to boiler design, and the help of the builders, the North British Locomotive Co.

Further application of Swindon principles to power problems much different in type and size to anything in the GWR were brought to the LMS in 1932 by Stanier, who early in his tenure conceived the plan of a few standard classes on the lines of Churchward's ideas 30 years before, but at first close applications of Swindon notions on superheat led to near disaster. In reverse, Stanier allowed some of his assistants to tamper with valve events, and not for some years did the GWR lap:lead ratios find a place. Stanier's succession of engines – the two-cylinder 2-8-0s, two- and three-cylinder 4-6-0s, four-cylinder Pacifics, and the lesser breeds of 2-6-0s and 2-6-4Ts, and the numbers constructed by LMS works and outside builders – revolutionised LMS motive-power before World War II; his personality revolutionised the whole mechanical-engineering department and made it a pleasant place wherein to work.

The years 1932-9 formed the heyday of British locomotives – as locomotives. Only in the fundamental relations of steam reciprocating locomotives to a complete railway system, in the science of railway mechanics, and in overall economics, did the balance fail, as touched on briefly in Chapter 1.

By 1938 the express engines of the four Groups were hauling nearly 200 trains a day at start-to-stop speeds of 58 to 72mph and totalling about 18,000 miles, and were of such reliability that an engine could work these services day after day for 30, 40, and even 50 days on end. Punctuality was to a standard never attained since. Coal consumptions per

Fig 22
LMS two-cylinder Hughes-Fowler 2-6-0s known generally as the Horwich Crabs, and one of the most successful pre-1932 types of the biggest group company; first built 1926

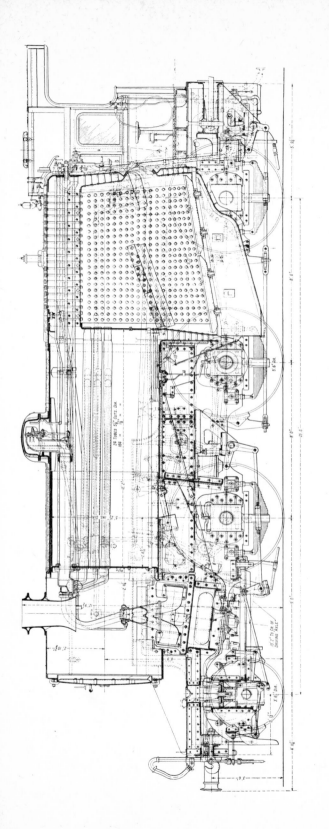

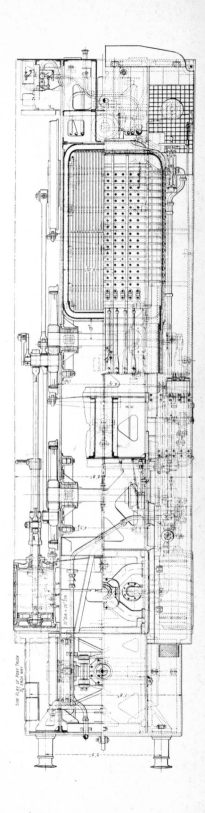

mile and per ton-mile were far lower than those of any pre-Group engines off the GWR, and ton-miles per engine hour were correspondingly higher. 500-ton trains operated over generally level routes at scheduled speeds of 56-58mph on coal consumptions of 40-42lb/mile, a result of the combination of advanced balanced design and keen and skilful driving and firing. The morale of whole railway staffs reached its peak before World War II.

Locomotives handling these services and other important main-line workings were 4-6-2, 4-6-0 and 2-6-2, with powerful modern 4-4-0s in echelon on the LNER and SR; the last Atlantics to be built were Nos 509-10 of the NBR in 1921. The big engines were mainly the three- and four-cylinder forms, but apart from the LNER and one class on the SR the powerful 2-6-0 and 4-6-0 mixed-traffic engines that were such a feature of Group years had only two outside cylinders. Two inside cylinders were applied in new construction only to 0-6-0s and a few six-coupled tanks after 1931. From that year

the 0-8-0 disappeared from new orders in favour of 2-8-0s or large 0-6-0s of 57-58 tons weight.

All types had ample steam-generating capacity, helped in large wide-firebox 4-6-2s and 2-6-2s by combustion-chambers (see Chapter 7). Steam pressures were 220 to 250psi, but final steam temperatures in normal working were rarely above 580 to 600°F (310-315°C). Axiomatic was the freest possible steam flow through regulator, dry pipe, superheater, steam pipes, valves, cylinders, exhaust, blast pipe and chimney, along with valve proportions, events and settings that permitted high-expansive working without over-compression. Chapelon's ideas on exhaust were incorporated in several engines from LNER *Cock o' the North* onwards. All these features in combination with adequate boiler power permitted the astonishing crop of three-figure peak speeds that were almost a daily feature of the LNER streamlined Coronation turn and culminated in *Mallard*'s 125mph on brake trials in July 1938. Free running with heavy trains on moderate or low fuel consumptions was universal. Balancing was greatly improved, and riding was reasonable when new; no 4-4-0 or 4-6-0 gave unruffled motion when there was lateral wear in the trailing boxes and horns, but most 4-6-2s were good as vehicles, par-

Streamlined class A4 Pacific *Mallard* on the brake test train at Barkston on 3 July 1938 an hour before attaining the world record speed for steam traction of 126mph. (H. M. Hoather)

ticularly the LNER streamlined A4s.

Common problems were steam leakage past piston valves until 1928-30 (see Chapter 6) and smoke and steam drift from 1928-30. The latter, undreamed of by the men who designed and drove the fire-throwers of 1903-23, was experienced as soon as the whole valve, exhaust and front-end systems were improved so that short cut-offs could be used normally. The SR was the first to suffer, and by the end of 1927 the King Arthurs were being fitted with side deflector plates coming up as far as boiler centre line. Eventually Maunsell put them on Lord Nelsons, Schools, mixed-traffic 4-6-0s, some of the 2-6-0s and other engines, but no major endeavour was made to fit them quickly. The LMS Royal Scots went through the same phases, but after the Leighton Buzzard accident in 1931 all 70 engines were given side deflector plates rapidly. The Rebuilt Royal Scots in the 1940s also began without deflectors but were soon given them, though taper boilers generally seemed to create air currents that prevented constant smoke drift.

Applying some of Chapelon's exhaust ideas, Gresley felt Cock o' the North might well need deflector plates and out of this and the immediately following streamlining tests grew the streamlined front end applied to the A4 Pacifics and P2-class 2-8-2s that was just as effective in smoke lifting as in power saving at high speed. The 'Hush-Hush' compound 4-6-2-2 No 10000 was the first of all and from being turned out in 1929 had an effective combination of smoke-lifting side wings merging into an aerodynamical shroud. This was the first British tender engine in which the locomotive alone weighed over 100 tons. Side shields otherwise were unknown on the LNER until the Thompson and Peppercorn Pacifics of 1945-8. The LMS Pacifics with single blast nozzles had no deflector plates, but the Duchess-City batches with plain double blast pipes were given side deflectors when not streamlined. Smoke and steam drift prevention was also a reason for the form of shroud devised for the Bulleid Pacifics on the SR.

Limited maximum cut-off became widespread though not to the 50 per cent practised in the USA in the Lima super-power 2-8-4s and 2-10-4s. Gresley steadily kept to 65 per cent, but the combination of this with three cylinders at 120° angles did not always give good starting, and during the war years his successor began to adjust the valve and reversing gear to give 75 per cent. The Bulleid Pacifics had 70 per cent; many Stanier engines had 70 to 77 per cent, and numerous engines on the LMS and GWR did not exceed 77-78 per cent whereas 80 to 83 per cent was common in the older short-lap short-travel designs.

Contributing to the general standard of performance between 1932 and 1939 was the reduced resistance of rolling stock and locomotives. The former was due to better mechanical design, lower weight per seat, smoother sides, and greater uniformity of contour in the stock down a train. Lower resistance per ton of locomotive weight was due mainly to reduced *internal* resistance resulting from better conditions of steam and exhaust flow, but in part also the greater rigidity of chassis and ability to maintain that rigidity by less wear in service. Resistance of multi-cylinder large-wheel six-coupled express engines which around 1913-14 had been of the order of 20lb/ton at 40mph and 34lb/ton at 70mph along the straight level had come down by 1939 to around 12 and 25lb/ton respectively.

Compounding really had no effective part in Group practice. On 1 January 1923 no fewer than 98 Webb engines were still running as compounds, as were 11 LYR 0-8-0s plus 45 Midland 4-4-0s on the LMS and seven Atlantics plus two other engines on the LNER. Apart from another 195 of the Midland design built 1924-32, the only compounds constructed in Group years were the Hughes 4-6-0 No 10456 on the LMS and the 4-6-2-2 No 10000 with 450psi pressure in a Yarrow water-tube boiler on the LNER. This was largely because compound engines as designed, driven and used in Britain could show nothing quantitive over single-expansion engines of 225-250psi with well-designed valves, motion and steam flow; but the Midland-type compounds did tend to indicate more even turning moment with less wear in boxes and horns, a gentler blast on the fire, less leakage through valves and past pistons, and a reasonable comparative repair cost. The trouble on the LMS was that they were not nearly big enough for the conditions.

The importance which at last was accorded free steam flow and proper valve events, and which in certain designs led to twin (LMS) or multi-jet (SR) or Kylchap (LNER) exhaust systems, had two other results. First was the realisation that a few inches in wheel diameter were neither here nor there and that wheels of 6ft to 6ft 3in would turn as freely as those of 6ft 9in. This appreciation led in later Group years to the Bulleid Pacifics with 6ft 2in wheels which could run up to 80mph almost of themselves, and were reputed to have touched 100mph on occasions, equal to 7.5 revs/sec.

Secondly, possible improvements over even the best long-lap long-travel piston valves were sought on the LNER and LMS by using poppet valves as detailed in Chapter 6. Maintenance costs of the LNER poppet-valve installations always were said to be cheaper than those of piston valves and Walschaerts motion, but the independence of cylinder events that could be achieved by the poppet valve gears of the early 1930s did not give sufficient advantage over large piston valves that had something near optimum valve events and ratios.

General maintenance and repair costs of the best locomotives were not low or anything like it in those years before World War I, and weak frame structures were one recurrent cause of expense; but the work was done promptly and effectively on the whole. Shop practices and equipment were developed continuously. In particular, much more use came to be made of portable or semi-portable electrically and pneumatically driven machines for drilling, drilling out, tapping, reaming, expanding, knocking out rivets and grinding; these machines were used most on the repair work that nominally constituted 80 to 100 per cent of the activity in a railway-owned plant. A reversal of procedure of bringing the tool to the work rather than the work to the tool was scarcely involved, but boilers and other large components could be moved through a single-line flow with semi-portable machines on frames at each stage. From this period also dates the Zeiss-optical method of frame erection introduced at Swindon, and also generally closer tolerances in machining and erection, and the beginnings towards the end of the LMS of the first comprehensive limits-and-fits system.

Mileages did not reach American standards, though several of the express types on big-mileage turns ran 80,000 miles a year and more for several years until the war put an end to such things. That figure represented also approximately the mileage between heavy repairs if there was little in the way of intermediates, but some classes like the GWR 4700-class large-wheel 2-8-0 regularly went 100,000 miles between shoppings.

In pre-1914 days GWR four-cylinder Stars had gone 120,000 miles between major shoppings whereas the 6ft 8in two-cylinder 4-6-0s with 30in stroke and inferior balancing did not exceed 85,000 miles. Rather later the early Gresley Pacifics went over 100,000 miles, but gradual increase in train weights and speeds, meaning an increase in load factor, brought this value down 10 to 20 per cent.

However, the more usual procedure on top-class engines by 1938 was to withdraw pistons and valves at sheds for examination every 40,000 to 45,000 miles; give an intermediate repair, especially to wheels, axleboxes and driving gear, at 75,000 to 100,000 miles; and a heavy repair, including boiler work, at 150,000 to 200,000 miles, when the engine would be in the shops for 15 to 22 days and out of traffic for 20 to 30 days. Between times, according largely to the water quality, the engines would have one day off in nine to 16 for boiler washout, routine examination and minor repairs.

Throughout their lives well-known Group and pre-Group classes had annual averages up to 60,000 miles, which is to be considered good in view of the long war conditions and the labour situation throughout the time of BR. The GWR Castles of the 1920s averaged around 50,000mpa through a life of 35-37 years; the Kings of the late 1920s made around 55,000mpa through 30 to 34 years of life; Gresley's Pacifics of 1922-4 had a greater spread over some 30 to 40 working years, varying from 50,-000 to 65,000mpa; Royal Scots made up to 55,000mpa taken over a 35-year life but this included the time after rebuilding; Princess Royal Pacifics averaged nearly 55,000mpa over 26-27 years; and 26 out of the 38 Coronation-Duchess Pacifics on the LMS over 18 to 26 years of life averaged above 60,000mpa with a top above 70,000.

No GWR Castle or King actually attained 2 million miles in service. A few of the Gresley A1 Pacifics did; so did a handful of Royal Scots, but in this last case there was little left of the original after the complete reconstruction. In all the engines mentioned above, the changes of boilers and other parts from the standardisation schemes gave total mileage figures that had little significance.

Some part of the increasing complexity of locomotives helped to increase mileage or decrease the time under examination and repair, such as sand guns, rocking grates, blow-down cocks or continuous blow-down, ashpan drench cocks and the like. This was helped also by equipment not on the locomotive, such as hot-water washing-out plant, mechanical coalers, water softeners, and revised plant and procedure in sheds and shops.

Locomotive construction costs rose slowly but steadily through the 17 years of Grouping from 1923 and then went up sharply. The charged cost varied partly according to the number of engines marked with the whole cost of development, drawings, patterns and flanging blocks. Gresley's two GNR Pacifics at a time of high material prices cost £12,350 per engine and tender with all charges absorbed. The next 10 of 1923 were marked at £7614 apiece, or around £70/ton of empty weight. The Glasgow-built Gresley Pacifics of 1924-5 from a private contractor were priced at £8720 but a full set of drawings was supplied from Doncaster.

The 50 Royal Scots were supplied from NBL at £7725 each including the preparation of all drawings, but only a slight profit accrued to the builder. Crewe's price for the 10 Princess Royal Pacifics of 1935 was given as £8538 each, but all the development and similar charges were entered against the first two engines of 1933, which cost £24,300 for the two. The five streamlined Coronation Pacifics of 1937 had Crewe costs of £11,813 apiece, but the succeeding engines of 1938-9 were marked only at £9500 per engine and tender, or £82½/ton of empty weight. Swindon's price for the

**Table 6  Performance Data of Group and BR Locomotives**

| Locomotive | Route | Trailing loads | Schedule speed | Coal cons | Firing rate | Coal cons | Coal cons | Evap rate |
|---|---|---|---|---|---|---|---|---|
| | | tons | mph | lb/mile | lb/sfg/hr | lb/ ton-mile[1] | lb/ dbhphr | lb steam/ lb coal |
| LNWR Claughton  4-cyl  4-6-0 | London-Carlisle | 395 | 51 | 46.6 | 79 | 0.101 | 5.03 | 6.9 |
| GWR Castle  4-cyl  4-6-0 | Swindon-Plymouth | 475-285[2] | 50 | 43.5 | 68 | 0.101 | 2.83 | 9.9 |
| LMSR Royal Scot  3-cyl  4-6-0 | London-Carlisle | 440 | 52 | 37 | 62.5 | 0.066 | 3.25 | 8.1 |
| LMSR Class 5  2-cyl  4-6-0 | London-Leeds | 290 | 52 | 49.5 | 74 | 0.098 | 3.17 | 7.7 |
| LMSR Coronation  4-cyl  4-6-2 | London-Glasgow | 330[3] | 60 | 39.2 | 47.3 | 0.080 | 3.03 | 8.2 |
| LMSR Duchess  4-cyl  4-6-2 | Crewe-Glasgow | 605 | 55 | 68.7 | 75.7 | 0.091 | 3.12 | 7.7 |
| LNER/BR No 60114  3-cyl  4-6-2 | London-Grantham | 600 | 52 | 47.5 | 57 | 0.079 | 2.41 | 7.5 |
| BR Britannia  2-cyl  4-6-2 | General tests | 500 | 70[5] | 43 | 75 | 0.075 | 2.4 | 8.0 |
| BR Class 9  2-cyl  2-10-0 | Appleby-Aisgill[4] | 640 | 33 | 88 | 72.5 | 0.114 | 2.64 | 8.0 |
| LMSR Turbomotive  4-6-2 | London-Liverpool | 485 | 55 | 41.6 | 50.7 | 0.067 | 2.78 | 8.9 |

[1] per gross ton-mile, including loco and tender    [2] 285 tons over Newton Abbot-Plymouth section with 1 in 36-50 grades    [3] Streamline loco and train    [4] All uphill, mostly at 1 in 100    [5] Steady test speed

first batch of four-cylinder 4-6-0 Castles in 1923-4 was £6841 each, and for the first batch of Kings in 1927 was £7419, or £72/ton of empty weight.

A defect of steam reciprocating locomotives to the end was the low possible thermal efficiency. Under optimum conditions on test a superheated compound could peak an ihp thermal efficiency above 11 per cent and a similar single-expansion locomotive nearly 10 per cent. In service the indicated value could not reach 9 per cent, and on long non-stop runs the drawbar thermal efficiency was only $6\frac{1}{4}/6\frac{1}{2}$ per cent. Many locomotives did their daily work at less than half that figure. Nevertheless these values were well in advance of the $6\frac{3}{4}$ per cent indicated and 5 per cent drawbar efficiencies of the superheated short-lap short-travel engines of 1912-14.

Road tests of a GWR Castle in 1924 showed 8.22 per cent *indicated* thermal efficiency. This was the

The LMS Stanier Class 5 4-6-0; it could go almost anywhere and do almost anything. (L & GRP)

best engine of its time, and it is a mark of the improvement effected in the Group era that by 1939 many engines on other lines had values within 5 to 10 per cent of those taken over many miles of service (see Table 6). Engines in the table were all main-line types; no means were ever found of improving substantially the daily thermal efficiency of that 90 per cent not engaged in top-link duties.

A few attempts were made to raise the ceiling of thermal efficiency by high-pressure and super-pressure (LNER No 10000 and LMS *Fury*) and by steam turbine locomotives (Reid-Ramsay 1909-10; Ramsay 1921-2; Reid-Macleod 1926-7; Beyer Peacock Ljungstrom 1926-7), but none met with any success. Only the LMS Turbomotive No 6202 achieved practical work and, for a non-reciprocating steam locomotive, did extremely well and made a total mileage of 458,772 before withdrawal in 1950. Nevertheless it made this effective work largely by elimination of that feature of the turbine, the condenser, which was mainly responsible for the higher thermal efficiency. Nevertheless its coal consump-

tion per dbhphr was about 6½ per cent less than that of the LMS Princess Royal Pacifics, which were the best LMS engines in that respect.

Locomotive power and output during the first 16 years of Grouping rose by almost 100 per cent. The 1250dbhp and around 1550ihp at about 60mph of the GWR four-cylinder 4-6-0s that were exceptional before 1923 rose by 1939 to maxima of 1800dbhp and 2300ihp in several classes. Gresley's 2-8-2 *Cock o' the North* got up to 2800ihp on Vitry test bank in France in 1934, and brief peaks above 3000ihp were attained by LMS Duchess Pacifics, the most powerful of all British passenger locomotives, and responsible for the most outstanding speed and haulage performance recorded. This was the test run in 1939 when non-streamlined No 6234 with double chimney took a 604-ton trailing load over the 486-- mile round trip between Crewe and Glasgow at 55mph average speed, and with average coal consumptions of 69lb/mile, 76lb/sfg/hr, 3.12lb/dbhphr, and 0.091lb/ton-mile. Maximum dbhp was 2510 when accelerating up 1 in 130 at 42mph, and corresponding ihp was above 3300. The cut-off at the time was 35 per cent.

Group features not yet emphasised included the streamlining of selected passenger engines and trains for what were then super end-to-end speeds; the large scale construction of powerful mixed-traffic engines; and the reduced scale of tank engine

Three-cylinder RC poppet-valve 2-8-2 built in 1934 for the Edinburgh-Aberdeen services. It was the heaviest tender locomotive ever used in Britain, 110.7 tons locomotive only.

building.

Streamlining was confined essentially to the 35 LNER A4-class Pacifics and 24 of the LMS Pacifics, though 11 of the latter appeared after war began and so were never used on very fast trains. The A4s retained their shrouds to the last though the side valances were removed early in the war. The LMS engines were de-streamlined in 1946-7 but for several years the sloping smokebox tops remained. Saving in power by streamlining the whole Silver Jubilee train was given as about 100hp at 90mph, but the 240-ton train required an average of only 640dbhp for its 70mph journey to Darlington.

Mixed-traffic requirements were handled in different ways by the four Groups. The SR 2-6-0s and 4-6-0s grew up from pre-1923 designs. The GWR took a step long contemplated of supplementing and replacing the standard Moguls by 4-6-0s of greater boiler capacity. This brought forth the Halls with 6ft wheels and a standard No 1 boiler in 1928 after the prototype *St. Martin* conversion in 1924, and later to the Grange class with the same boiler and cylinders but 5ft 8in wheels, and then in 1938 to the Manors, with ½in off the cylinders, the same wheels and a smaller boiler. Some of the two last-named classes had coupled wheels and motion parts from withdrawn 2-6-0s. Altogether 440 of these three types were built at Swindon between 1928 and 1950.

Mixed-traffic policies quite different from one another were followed by the LMS and LNER. From 1933 the former concentrated almost entirely on the two-cylinder class 5 design with 6ft wheels which could travel over 70 per cent of the route

LMS Stanier two-cylinder 2-6-4T for passenger work.

Three-cylinder *Green Arrow* 2-6-2 mixed-traffic locomotive with 22 tons axle load, LNER, 1936.

mileage. Over 700 were built in LMS days and brought the nearest practical approach to the operating department's demand for a locomotive that would do anything and go anywhere. The LNER, on the other hand, after building for years three-cylinder Moguls with 20-ton axle load took up the Green Arrow three-cylinder 2-6-2 with 22-ton axle load that could travel over only 43 per cent of the route mileage but was a distinct help on heavy mainline duties. During the war years was introduced the smaller B1-class 4-6-0 that could work over 65 per cent of the mileage but was unable to take any part in real main-line haulage.

Large tank engine construction on the LMS began with the 10 four-cylinder 4-6-4Ts based on the LYR 4-6-0 tender engines, but they had a life of but 14 to 18 years on restricted services. A much better two-cylinder 2-6-4T followed under Fowler and was developed in two- and three-cylinder versions right through to BR times, from Stanier's day with taper boilers. Only two tank designs were evolved by the LNER, the Gresley three-cylinder

V1-class 2-6-2T and Thompson's much heavier L1-class two-cylinder 2-6-4T, the former for local passenger turns and the latter for mixed duties. The GWR 0-6-2T to new design, and developments of the standard 0-6-0PT, were built by outside makers as well as at Swindon, including 250 of the latter from outside works in 1928-31. The 0-6-0PT, a standard from pre-Churchward times, was changed at the very end of GWR existence from inside cylinders and Stephenson motion to outside cylinders and Walschaerts motion. One other GWR tank activity was the rebuilding of Churchward 2-8-0Ts to 2-8-2T form with 6-ton coal bunkers that enabled them to run on occasions with coal trains from Severn Tunnel Junction to London.

Small interest was shown by the Group lines in the Garratt. The LNER 2-8-0 + 0-8-2 six-cylinder banker of 1925 did its work well enough but was perhaps above the size needed. The 33 LMS 2-6-0 + 0-6-2s were ruined as to general performance and mileage between repairs by ex-Midland insistence on small bearings, short-lap short-travel valves and

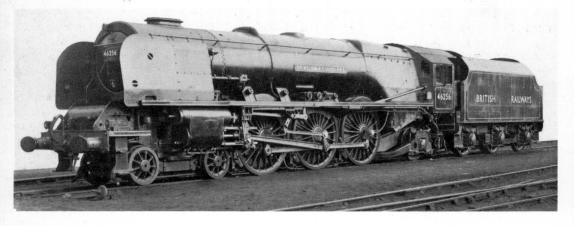

Heaviest locomotive of any type used in Britain, the LNER's 178-ton Beyer-Garratt banker of 1925.

War Department 2-8-0 based on Stanier's LMS standard Class 8 but with air brakes and other modified details. (Mitchell Library)

The last two LMS Coronation Pacifics Nos 6256/7 delivered in 1947/8 with Ivatt detail improvements to the original Stanier design perhaps represented the peak of British steam locomotive development. (British Railways)

standard mechanical portion details based on Fowler 0-6-0s and the Derby-designed 2-8-0s of the Somerset & Dorset.

Like the years 1914-19, so those of 1939-45 changed the railway system irrevocably. On the locomotive side the existing regimes came to an end early in the war, for Gresley died in April 1941, Collett retired the same year, and Stanier was seconded to government service in 1942 and officially retired from the LMS in 1944 without returning to active service. Bulleid had succeeded Maunsell in the autumn of 1937.

Vital need for minimum inspection and maintenance and maximum reliability led to simplification, and with the exception of the Bulleid Pacifics and one or two engines for which material was already in hand the locomotives built during the war and just afterwards had two outside cylinders and were mainly for freight or mixed traffic; extensive and important rebuilding programmes on multi-cylinder types were initiated on the LNER (Gresley's Mikados to Pacifics) and LMS (Royal Scots to rebuilt Royal Scots). Most important new design of the war was the Thompson B1 4-6-0 on the LNER, but in 1945 appeared the first of a new GWR express 4-6-0, the two-cylinder County class of which 30 were built 1945-7.

Before the Group era ended 10-coupled engines began to run on regular freight and passenger services for the first time. These were the Ministry of Supply 2-10-0s with an axle load limited to 13½ tons for overseas service. They were the first normal engines to have a wide firebox spread out over the tops of the coupled wheels, and the first for 80 years to have rocking grates. On nationalisation 25 were taken into BR stock. Of much greater application were the Ministry standard 2-8-0s based in a general way on wartime austerity principles, which ran on the Group lines before nationalisation and of which 733 were taken into BR stock. Finally, 75 of the Ministry's so-called 'Austerity Tanks', 0-6-0ST

Rebuilt Royal Scot, a redesign dating from 1943 and applied eventually to all 70 locomotives of the original 1927 class. (British Railways)

| Table 7 Performance Data, LNER(BR) 4-6-2 No 60114 | | |
|---|---|---|
| Route | London-Leeds | London-Grantham |
| Trailing load    tons | 500 | 600 |
| Average running speed    mph | 51.6 | 52.7 |
| Coal consumption    lb/mile | 40 | 47.5 |
| Firing rate    lb/sfg/hr | 47.8 | 57 |
| Coal consumption    lb/dbhphr | 3.1 | 2.41 |
| Evaporation    lb steam/lb coal | 7.9 | 7.54 |
| Average final steam temp    °F | 536 | 550 |
| Average smokebox gas temp    °F | 540 | 568 |
| Drawbar thermal efficiency    % | 6.28 | 6.5 |
| Average dbbh throughout trips | 803 | 1031[1] |

[1] Max short-time output 2150 dbhp @ 40% cut-off

with cast iron wheels, were purchased by the LNER and came into possession of BR.

In the immediate post-war years Bulleid put in hand on the SR the lighter West Country Pacifics based on the Merchant Navy design and managed to have 110 built between 1945 and the end of 1948. Sober and righteous men resisted his proposals to build 30 Leader-class 0-6-6-0s with sleeve-valve cylinders, gear drive, et al, and only one was completed. On the LNER a number of Peppercorn three-cylinder Pacifics with two different wheel sizes were put in hand, but the 6ft 8in size was not at work until after nationalisation. In them Gresley's standard 41sq ft grate area for Pacifics was increased to the 50 sq ft of the Mikados and the concentrated drive was replaced by divided drive along with three sets of valve motion.

H. G. Ivatt on the LMS held back the last two Stanier-type Pacifics, authorised in 1945, and put on them (Nos 6256-7) grease-lubricated roller-bearing axleboxes throughout engine and tender, self-cleaning smokeboxes, rocking grates, hopper ashpans, a new convenient form of screw reverse, cab-operated blow-off cocks, a cast steel one-piece Delta trailing truck frame, and manganese-steel

liners to coupled boxes and horns. The last-named had already been used on the LMS, and along with the pin-joint horn cross ties gave great frame rigidity that could be maintained almost without wear. In times of much tribulation these two engines went 96,000 miles to first intermediate shopping followed by another 90,000 miles to first main repair.

Many of these features were adopted also for Ivatt's new 2-6-0s and 2-6-2Ts and revised 4-6-0s and 2-6-4Ts built on the bases of existing LMS standards to give locomotives for secondary services the benefit of latest main-line practice. In this activity was included that one class 5 4-6-0 No 4767 with outside Stephenson motion.

This review of 25 years of Group locomotive development concludes with a reference to the service performance of almost the last Group passenger type, the LNER Peppercorn three-cylinder A1-class 4-6-2. The results shown in Table 7 were from normal train service with a dynamometer car attached. With lighter trains of 375 to 400 tons the difficulty was to keep the grate evenly covered, for 50sq ft of grate was too much for such duties and 500-ton loads could not always be provided. Thus at the beginning of the Group lines the locomotives generally were too small for the needs; at the end of the period they were tending to be too large for the schedules and loads, and the size was warranted only by the much reduced skill and morale in handling and maintenance.

# 12  National Finale

On 1 January 1948 British Railways took over from the four Groups 20,026 steam locomotives in service stock, of 33 different wheel arrangements in over 200 classes, and in quantities as listed in Table 8. Virtually all these, plus about 1500 built subsequently, were gone 20 years later.

The decision to concentrate on steam power for the new system was taken on the basis of conservative thought buttressed conveniently by a great disparity in capital costs, for any new main-line diesels that could come from industry would be prototypes at four times the price of the steam locomotives they would replace, and the cost of the latter by then was over £150/ton of empty weight, or nearly twice the pre-war figures as given in Chapter 11.

A study of leading steam types for construction by BR was initiated under the new mechanical-engineering headquarters, composed mainly of ex-LMS personnel, and was forwarded by the well-publicised Interchange Trials of 1948 between 14 different locomotives from the BR regions that succeeded the four Group companies.

Contrasted with the results obtained pre-war as summarised in Table 6 (Chapter 11) the 1948 trials showed coal consumptions per dbhphr of: Merchant Navy Pacific 3.6lb, King 4-6-0 3.57lb, Rebuilt Royal Scot 3.38lb, LMS Coronation Pacific 3.12lb, Gresley A4 Pacific 3.06lb. In the mixed traffic class the LMS class 4-6-0 showed 3.54lb, the LNER Thompson B1 4-6-0 3.59lb, the GWR Hall 3.94lb, and the Bulleid West Country Pacific 4.11lb. Unit evaporations (lb water/lb coal) were: Merchant Navy 8.45, King 8.07, West Country 7.94, A4 Pacific 7.92, class 5 4-6-0 7.92, Rebuilt Royal Scot 7.7, GWR Hall 7.69 and Thompson B1 7.68.

In general the locomotives of no region stood out on all counts above the others, and building programmes of the first two years were confined to Group types, some of which were already on order. By June 1948 a series of 12 new standard types was put up for construction from 1951 onwards, and 160, of six different classes, were included in that year's programme, the number being limited by the first of the government financial scares, though around 400 new locomotives a year were needed to keep the whole stock in good order.

Only five of the proposed standards were to completely new designs. Under H. G. Ivatt the LMS in its last years had introduced modern types for secondary service which were taken as the bases for the new low-power BR standards (class 4 2-6-0, class 3

| Wheel Arrgt | GWR | LNER | LMSR | SR | BR Total |
|---|---|---|---|---|---|
| **Tender Engines** | | | | | |
| 4-6-2-2 | | 1 | | | 1 |
| 4-6-2 | | 139 | 50 | 90 | 279 |
| 4-6-0 | 675 | 547 | 1104 | 177 | 2503 |
| 4-4-2 | | 55 | | 9 | 64 |
| 4-4-0 | 85 | 507 | 651 | 372 | 1615 |
| 2-8-0 | 221 | 681 | 567 | | 1469 |
| 2-6-2 | | 186 | | | 186 |
| 2-6-0 | 253 | 274 | 308 | 174 | 1009 |
| 2-4-0 | 3 | 18 | 3 | | 24 |
| 0-10-0 | | | 1 | | 1 |
| 0-8-0 | | 246 | 706 | | 952 |
| 0-6-0 | 183 | 1698 | 2180 | 322 | 4383 |
| 0-4-2 | | | | 4 | 4 |
| Totals | 1420 | 4352 | 5570 | 1148 | 12490 |
| **Tank Engines** | | | | | |
| 4-8-0T | | 13 | | 4 ? | 17 |
| 4-6-2T | | 117 | 10 | 7 | 134 |
| 4-4-2T | | 152 | 68 | 47 | 267 |
| 2-8-8-2 [2] | | 1 | | | 1 |
| 2-6-6-2 [2] | | | 33 | | 33 |
| 2-8-2T | 54 | | | | 54 |
| 2-8-0T | 151 | | | | 151 |
| 2-6-4T | | 22 | 498 | 15 | 535 |
| 2-6-2T | 458 | 92 | 219 | | 769 |
| 2-4-2T | | 118 | 167 | | 285 |
| 2-4-0T | 13 | | 1 | 3 | 17 |
| 0-8-4T | | 6 | 14 | | 20 |
| 0-8-2T | 1 | | 9 | | 10 |
| 0-8-0T | | 13 | | 9 | 22 |
| 0-6-4T | | 2 | | 5 | 7 |
| 0-6-2T | 391 | 619 | 94 | 142 | 1246 |
| 0-6-0T | 1251 | 818 | 864 | 124 | 3057 |
| 0-4-4T | | 110 | 193 | 287 | 590 |
| 0-4-2T | 100 | 4 | 3 | 18 | 125 |
| 0-4-0T | 17 | 88 | 62 | 29 | 196 |
| Totals | 2436 | 2175 | 2235 | 690 | 7536 |
| Total: Tender & Tank | 3856 | 6527 | 7805 | 1838 | 20026 |

Table 8  British Railways Locomotives, 1 January 1948 [1]

[1] Service stock   [2] Beyer-Garratt

2-6-0, class 2 2-6-0, class 4 2-6-4T, class 3 2-6-2T, and class 2 2-6-2T) and the larger Stanier-Ivatt class 5 4-6-0 was perpetuated, all with detail changes to bring them within the standard requirements. The new designs were the class 7 and class 6 Pacifics (Britannias and Clans), the class 4 4-6-0 (75000 series) with 17-ton axle load, the class 9 2-10-0, and the single class 8 Pacific No 71000.

All except the last-named were considered as mixed-traffic types. This, and a wide route availability based on axle load, linear loading and loading gauge were leading points in the locomotive policy adopted. Others were standardisation of components; simplicity and minimum number of moving parts particularly by limitation to two cylinders; ease of access for inspection and maintenance; good main bearing performance, by roller bearing boxes when advantageous; maintenance of original squareness by rigid structures with minimum wear; fittings such as rocking grates, hopper ashpans and self-cleaning smokeboxes to ease disposal; large grates; high evaporative power; something approaching a standard cab layout; and a high factor of adhesion with a sensitive regulator to minimise

British Railways Class 7 Britannia Pacific, the first BR standard to appear, 1951.

slipping; long-lap long-travel valves; and high superheat.

These requirements were entirely in accord with the times. Never again would general driving, firing and shed morale and skill reach the pitch of the last pre-war years. No longer were ever higher outputs and speed with ever lower coal consumptions the criteria. The aims were simply an ability to work mileages between heavy repairs at least equal to those of pre-war years but under the much poorer all-round conditions, and to show good availability in the meantime. This the standard classes did; the Britannia Pacifics, for example, normally could go 120,000 miles between shoppings.

Some of the most important modifications to Group engines effected in BR days, in particular the Kylchap exhausts on Eastern Region Pacifics and the high superheat and twin exhausts on Western Region Kings and Castles also were made simply to retain pre-war standards under deteriorating conditions.

Through some months from June 1948 the dozen suggested standard designs were developed, and in this period detail design principles and fittings were selected and became outstanding features of the BR standard locomotives. The main frames, central above the axleboxes, and the substantial racking

Fig 23
General arrangement of the BR two-cylinder Britannia Pacific of the first batch of 25 set to work in 1951. Certain modifications were made in later engines, for example to rear end of cab, piston and rod in one piece, rectangular-section coupling rods, and, in Nos 70040-9, plain-bearing driving and coupled axleboxes, and a grate different from the Hulson type with 12 rocking sections as shown here

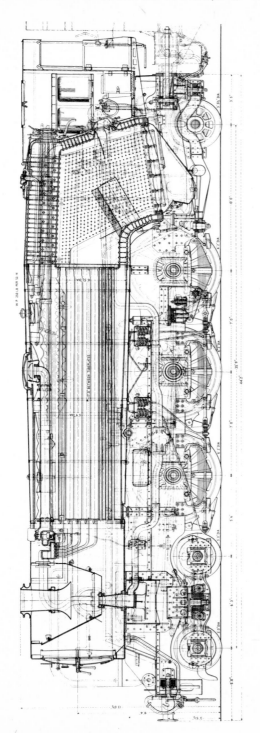

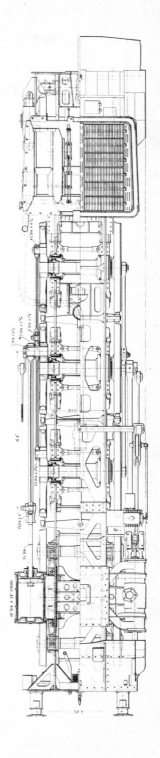

stays were pure Bulleid, as were the simple tyre fastening, the triple-section ashpan, and the trailing truck. Crosshead, slidebars and piston rod packing came from LNER details; suspension, rocking grate firedoor, big ends and general ensemble were based on LMS practice; and smokebox door, cylinder pressure-relief valves and other details came from the GWR.

Another contribution, but in a wider aspect, came from the war years when R. A. Riddles, the Railway Executive member for mechanical engineering, was in charge of Ministry of Supply locomotive production and other work. Under him the Stanier 2-8-0 had been modified slightly into a transition war-locomotive type and the Austerity 2-8-0s and 2-10-0s had been evolved. In this milieu, with many non-railway men in the personnel, Riddles had come to rocking grates and other details not common to British railways, and to the design of 10-coupled line-service engines, an experience that bore fruit when he gave instructions for the 12 standard BR designs to be drawn up. When difficulties arose in

getting a satisfactory design for the proposed 2-8-2 for heavy freights, Riddles put forward in its place the 2-10-0 that became the most successful of all BR standards.

A further postulate was that the recommendations of the Bridge Stress Committee's report of 1928 in regard to balancing should be observed as strictly as they had been in later Group days. This meant that at a speed of 5 revs/sec (or 0.9 of wheel-diameter speed) the hammer blow per axle should not exceed a quarter of the static axle load and that the summated hammer blow of the whole engine should not be above $12\frac{1}{2}$ tons. This was achieved by limiting to 40 per cent the proportion of reciprocating weights to be balanced in the larger types and 50 per cent in the smaller units. The Britannias showed hammer blows of 2.55 tons/axle and 6.6 tons for the whole engine at 5 revs/sec (66mph).

Preparation of the complete manufacturing drawings was complicated by the allocation of various drawing offices as parents for different complete classes plus responsibility for one or more particular components for all classes. For example, Brighton fathered the class 4 4-6-0 and class 4 2-6-4T engines and did brake and sanding gear for all classes. This was preferred to the establishment

British Railways Class 9 2-10-0, the last, and most numerous BR standard type to appear. *Evening Star* in 1960 was the last steam locomotive to be built for BR and the last to be built at Swindon. (British Railways)

**Table 9  Dimensions of British Railways Standard Steam Locomotives**

| | Class 8 4-6-2 | Class 7 4-6-2 | Class 6 4-6-2 | Class 5 4-6-0 | Class 4 4-6-0 | Class 4 2-6-0 | Class 3 2-6-0 | Class 2 2-6-0 | Class 4 2-6-4T | Class 3 2-6-2T | Class 2 2-6-2T | Class 9 2-10-0 |
|---|---|---|---|---|---|---|---|---|---|---|---|---|
| Cylinders (2)  in | 3 @ 18 x 28 | 20 x 28 | $19\frac{1}{2}$ x 28 | 19 x 28 | 18 x 28 | $17\frac{1}{2}$ x 26 | $17\frac{1}{2}$ x 26 | $16\frac{1}{2}$ x 24 | 18 x 28 | $17\frac{1}{2}$ x 26 | $16\frac{1}{2}$ x 24 | 20 x 28 |
| Boiler pressure  psi | 250 | 250 | 225 | 225 | 225 | 225 | 200 | 200 | 225 | 200 | 200 | 250 |
| Wheel dia  in | 74 | 74 | 74 | 74 | 68 | 63 | 63 | 60 | 68 | 63 | 60 | 60 |
| Boiler dias  in | $77\frac{1}{2}$/69 | $77\frac{1}{2}$/69 | 73/64 | $68\frac{1}{2}$/$59\frac{3}{4}$ | 63/57.5 | 63/57.5 | $60\frac{1}{2}$/53 | 56/51 | 63/57.5 | $60\frac{1}{2}$/53 | 56/51 | 73/69 |
| Tubes, no & od  in | 136 @ $2\frac{1}{8}$ | 136 @ $2\frac{1}{8}$ | 108 @ $2\frac{1}{8}$ | 151 @ $1\frac{7}{8}$ | 157 @ $1\frac{7}{8}$ | 154 @ $1\frac{5}{8}$ | 145 @ $1\frac{5}{8}$ | 162 @ $1\frac{5}{8}$ | 157 @ $1\frac{3}{4}$ | 145 @ $1\frac{5}{8}$ | 162 @ $1\frac{5}{8}$ | 138 @ 2 |
| Flues, no & od  in | 40 @ $5\frac{1}{2}$ | 40 @ $5\frac{1}{2}$ | 35 @ $5\frac{1}{2}$ | 28 @ $5\frac{1}{8}$ | 21 @ $5\frac{1}{8}$ | 24 @ $5\frac{1}{8}$ | 18 @ $5\frac{1}{8}$ | 12 @ $5\frac{1}{8}$ | 21 @ $5\frac{1}{8}$ | 18 @ $5\frac{1}{8}$ | 12 @ $5\frac{1}{8}$ | 35 @ $5\frac{1}{4}$ |
| Tube length  ft in | 17 - 0 | 17 - 0 | 17 - 0 | 13 - $2\frac{7}{8}$ | 13 - 0 | 10 - $10\frac{1}{2}$ | 10 - $10\frac{1}{2}$ | 10 - $10\frac{1}{2}$ | 12 - 3 | 10 - $10\frac{1}{2}$ | 10 - $10\frac{1}{2}$ | 15 - 3 |
| Evap hs: tubes and flues  sq ft | 2264 | 2264 | 1878 | 1479 | 1301 | 1061 | 933 | 924 | 1223 | 933 | 924 | 1836 |
| firebox  sq ft | 226 | 210 | 195 | 171 | 143 | 131 | 118 | 101 | 143 | 118 | 101 | 179 |
| total  sq ft | 2490 | 2474 | 2073 | 1650 | 1444 | 1192 | 1051 | 1025 | 1366 | 1051 | 1025 | 2015 |
| Grate area  sq ft | 48.6 | 42.0 | 36.0 | 28.6 | 26.7 | 23.0 | 20.3 | 17.5 | 26.7 | 20.3 | 17.5 | 40.2 |
| Superheating surface  sq ft | 691 | 704 | 628 | 369 | 265 | 254 | 190 | 134 | 246 | 190 | 134 | 535 |
| Max axle load  tons | 22.0 | 20.25 | 18.85 | 19.7 | 17.0 | 16.75 | 16.25 | 13.75 | 18.0 | 16.3 | 13.25 | 15.5 |
| Adhesion weight  tons | 66.0 | 60.75 | 56.4 | 55.05 | 51.0 | 49.6 | 48.5 | 40.5 | 55.05 | 48.75 | 39.25 | 77.5 |
| Loco weight, WO  tons | 101.25 | 94.0 | 88.5 | 73.0 | 67.9 | 59.1 | 57.45 | 49.25 | 88.65 | 74.05 | 63.25 | 86.7 |
| Engine + tender weight  tons | 156.75 | 141.2 | 135.7 | 120.2 | 110.1 | 101.25 | 99.6 | 86.1 | — | — | — | 142.0 |
| Tractive effort (75% b.p.)  lb | 35,000 | 28,400 | 24,250 | 23,050 | 22,150 | 21,340 | 19,000 | 16,350 | 22,150 | 19,000 | 16,350 | 35,000 |

of one large central drawing office, but it added enormously to time and trouble, and the first of all standard locomotives was not steamed until January 1951. Nevertheless, if steam traction was to be adopted the new standard designs had an advantage over perpetuation of Group designs, but they came so late and were comparatively so few in number that they had little measurable effect on total results. They are all too well known to warrant description; the leading dimensions are summarised in Table 9.

No four-coupleds, eight-coupleds or six-wheelers were included in the standard types. There was almost a preponderance of Pacifics and Moguls. The parts standardisation, though not neglected, was anything but complete, and seven boilers were needed to cover a dozen locomotive types. All engines, tender and tank, had taper boilers, and eight of the 12 classes had pressures of 225 or 250psi. Moreover there were seven cylinder variations. Cast steel cylinders with cast iron liners were common though not universal, the 18in by 28in size being of iron.

Most interesting reconstruction of the period was that of the 30 Merchant Navy Pacifics over the years 1955-9 and similar alteration of some of the

Rebuilt Merchant Navy Pacific, a major design and reconstruction activity of BR. (M. W. Earley)

lighter West Country class undertaken to get greater reliability and lower maintenance charges. The shroud and the chain-driven valve motion were replaced by normal boiler lagging and side smoke deflector plates and by three sets of Walschaerts motion; the inside cylinder casting (now of steel) and the crossheads were new, the piston valves were altered, the steam reversing was replaced by the BR screw type with only one cross shaft, and many other details were modified. The rebuilds lost none of the power and speed of the originals and gained greatly in availability and general effectiveness.

Replacement of Swindon superheaters by three-row Schmidt type on GWR Castles began in 1946 and in 1949 a change was made to four rows; from 1953 this became standard for all new or repaired Castle boilers. From 1957 plain twin exhausts were added, and engines equipped with these two modifications could give 3600lb drawbar pull at 86mph. Early in 1948 the first four-row superheaters were applied to the GWR Kings, followed in 1951 by a redesigned single blast pipe front end, and a drawbar pull of 7000lb at 70mph was a result. From 1955 BR standard double blast pipes brought the final stage in King development and made possible 1550dbhp sustained along the level at 60mph. But the above outputs were developed repeatedly by Castles and Kings in their

original states in the 1930s.

BR standard plain twin exhaust was fitted also to 73 of the 251 class 9 2-10-0s, and the highest-numbered engine of all, No 92250, was BR's only application (1959) of the Giesl exhaust system, and on Rugby test plant gave about 5 per cent increase in output and 5 per cent economy in coal. Three of the 10-coupled engines also were tried with mechanical stokers but the grates were too small for the equipment to be worthwhile, a factor that applied also to the larger grate of the Bulleid Pacific No 35005 on which similar equipment was tried in 1948-50.

Freer exhaust for the Gresley Pacifics on the Eastern Region was gained from 1957 by fitting Kylchap double exhaust to the 78 remaining ex-A1 and ex-A3 classes, by then all with 220psi boilers, and which was said to bring coal consumption down by 12 per cent to 45lb/mile on Anglo-Scottish trains of 500 tons, a figure effectively illuminating the deteriorating conditions, for the same duties had been worked in the 1930s at 42lb/mile. Kylchap exhaust was given also to the A4 streamliners from 1957, but here the effect was marked more in the

better condition of the engine rather than in enhanced power; in conjunction with piston and valve examinations every 36,000 miles (in place of 45,000 pre-war) the mileage between heavy repairs rose from the 75,000 miles of 1953-5 to 100,000 miles and more.

With thoughts of trying to cope with the chaotic coal situation trials with the Crosti boiler were sanction in 1953, but in place of a test on one or two engines a payment-by-results arrangement was adopted for 10 locomotives of the otherwise standard 2-10-0 type that were put into traffic in 1955. The results were anything but successful, largely because of great corrosion in the heater system, though the fear of having to pay the inventor considerable royalties on a sliding scale for any economy in coal above 12 per cent was a burden on nationalised minds. By 1958 the 10 engines were lying idle, but were rebuilt to normal with their rather smaller boilers.

A feature of BR practice was the comprehensive testing procedure possible after the opening of the Rugby stationary test plant in 1951 after nearly 30 years of proposals and efforts, and by the complete road testing given with the LMS mobile testing plant (something more than a mere dynamometer car, for it provided the equivalent of a counter-pressure locomotive also), and later with the

Last phase of the GWR Castle 4-6-0s, rebuilt in the 1950s by BR with double exhaust and four-row Schmidt superheater. (British Railways)

British Railways standard Class 5 4-6-0 with Caprotti valves; essentially the celebrated Stanier Black Five of the LMS. (British Railways)

Swindon-developed controlled road testing with normal dynamometer car. Essentially these came too late to be of any practical effect on a large scale, but they helped the design and modification of a few important classes and gave data of great retrospective interest.

The lightest BR Pacifics, the Clans, were disappointing, but though they had a route availability wider even than that of the class 5 4-6-0s they were not really necessary, and only the first batch of 10 was built. The largest engine of all, the 4-6-2 *Duke of Gloucester*, was not of the calibre of such pre-war types as the LMS Duchess and LNER A4 Pacifics. Certain standard classes developed a few faults, in particular the Britannias, with their wheel/axle vibration, hard riding and water carry-over difficulties; against the whole background these were of little moment.

No improvement was shown by the larger 4-6-2s and 4-6-0s over the level of performance of Group engines in the 1930s, for in the normal pressure and temperature ranges the ceilings of efficiency and capacity had already been attained, as had the general levelling-up to the highest standard, so that differences between locomotives of different companies were not so devastatingly marked as they were prior to 1923.

By the time of nationalisation the steam locomotive had reached its peak in a thermodynamic sense and had passed the peak of daily operational standards. There was no hope of further marked improvements, for the advantages of poppet valves could be only marginal, and the various efforts to economise in coal consumption or permit the use of poorer coal were proved impracticable for the conditions of the times. Nevertheless the operation and economy of British Railways lost nothing by the introduction of the dozen new standard classes.

But the BR stage was not a culmination of 150 years of British locomotive engineering; it was no more than a rearguard action that developed almost into a rout, for at no time from 1948 was BR authority, high or low, able to organise and insist on a standard of maintenance, repair and handling at all commensurate with the needs. Throughout nearly the whole of the BR period steam locomotives were operated under what, by previous standards, could only be called poor and ever-deteriorating maintenance conditions, a feature intensified as more and more diesels came on the line. The 'go as you please' of mid-Victorian years returned, but with a strong attitude of indifference and indiscipline added, so much so, that pre-1939 conditions remain unbelievable not only to enthusiasts but to many experienced railwaymen of the 1960s and 1970s. It is difficult to credit today the haulage, speed, coal consumptions, mileage, standards of driving and maintenance, and the punctuality sustained throughout the country at the apogee of the British locomotive – 1932-9.

Note No.                                                References

1 *Birmingham & South Staffordshire, or Illustrations of the History, Geology & Operations of a Mining District.*W. M. Hawkes Smith. 1838

2 No 2599, 24 March 1802. Richard Trevithick & Andrew Vivian

3 No 2632, 28 June 1802. Matthew Murray

4 *Life of Richard Trevithick.* Francis Trevithick. 1872

5 No 3431, 10 April 1811. John Blenkinsop

6 Watson Collection; North of England Institute of Mining & Mechanical Engineers, Newcastle

7 No 3632, 21 April 1812. Wm & E. W. Chapman

8 No 3666. 13 March 1813. Wm Hedley

9 First in *Treatise on Rail Roads.* Nicholas Wood. 1825

10 In the Science Museum

11 *Observations on the Comparative Merits of Locomotive and Fixed Engines.* Robert Stephenson & Joseph Locke. 1830

12 No 3887, 28 February 1815. Ralph Dodds & George Stephenson

13 No 4067, 13 September 1816. Wm Losh & George Stephenson

14 In the Science Museum

15 *Early Wooden Railways.* M. J. T. Lewis. 1970.

16 *Locomotive Profile* No 25

17 *Trans. of Newcomen Society,* Vol VII, February 1927

18 *Archiv für Bergbau und Hüttenwesen,* Vol XIX, 1829; translated and reproduced in part in *A Century of Locomotive Building 1823-1923.* J. G. H. Warren, and in *Trans. Newcomen Society* 1953.

19 Notebook of John Urpeth Rastrick. 1829

20 *Life of Robert Stephenson.* Vol I. J. C. Jeaffreson

21 *Locomotive Profile* No 7

22 *An Account of the Liverpool & Manchester Railway.* Henry Booth. 1830

23 *Practical Treatise on Locomotive Engines.* G. de Pambour. 1836

24 *Technics and Civilisation.* Lewis Mumford

25 *Description of Patent Locomotive Steam Engine.* W. P. Marshall. 1850. (Written 1838)

26 *Locomotive Profile* No 15

27 No 7745, 26 July 1838. John Gray

28 'Diaries of David Joy'. *The Railway Magazine* June 1908

29 *The Railway Magazine* August 1899, p. 104

30 *A Century of Locomotive Building 1823-1923.* J. G. H. Warren. 1923

31 No 8998, 23 June 1841. Robert Stephenson

32 *Railway Machinery.* D. K. Clark. 1855

33 No 9261, 15 February 1842. Thos R. Crampton

34 No 14107, 25 October 1884. David Joy

35 Act 7 Geo IV cap 49

36 Society of Engineers 1862

37 *The Engineer,* 1 October 1858, p. 255

38 Glasgow Institution of Engineers, 1862

39 Inst. of Mechanical Engineers, January 1861

40 *Proc. Inst. Civil Engineers,* Vol XVI, 1856

41 'Coal Without Smoke', paper to Soc. of Engineers 1862

42 *A Study of the Locomotive Boiler*

43 *Proc. Inst. Civil Engineers,* Vol XVI, 1856

44 *Proc. Inst. Mech. Engineers* 1866

45 No 6484, 7 October 1833. Robert Stephenson

46 *Locomotive Profile* No 1

47 To patent No 11086 of 1846; George Stephenson & Wm Howe

48 Report to canal shareholders *Present & Future Prospects of the Monmouthshire Canal.* Jas Brown. 1847

49 From 'Railway Accidents'; paper by Mark Huish. *Proc. Inst. Civil Engineers,* Vol II, 1851-2

50 *Locomotive Profile* No 15

51 *Locomotive Profile* No 27

52 *The Stirling Singles.* K. H. Leech & M. G. Boddy

53 *The Engineer,* 5 September 1862, p. 142

54 *Engineering,* 11 May 1894, p. 611

55 *Locomotive Profile* No 31

56 *The Decapod Locomotive of the GER.* W. O. Skeat. Trans. Newcomen Society, Vol XXVIII, 1952-3

57 *Proc. Inst. Mech. Engineers,* 14 December 1945

58 *Locomotive Profile* No 22

59 'A Modern Locomotive History'. E. S. Cox. *Journal Inst. Loco Engineers,* 1946

# Index